Collected by
Alexsys Thompson

GRATITUDE

A collection of short Stories;
expressing gratitude for the people
who make us who we are

Thank you to editors Darlena Eggebrecht and Rebecca
Thompson.

Published by Alexsys E Thompson 2019.

CONTENTS

This collection is dedicated to raising our human consciousness through gratitude.

Prologue from the Creator of Gratitude 540:

Alexsys Thompson

As with so many adventures in my life this book was born from a dream. My dreams had begun to manifest at a rapid pace over the past decade, in large part due to my own gratitude practice (yes, there is a lot of hard work in there, too). Once I was able to make the connection between my gratitude practice and living a life that was becoming more and more aligned with my purpose, I couldn't keep it to myself. I started talking to my loved ones about it, writing about it, and creating guided gratitude journals to support others in developing a gratitude practice. It is among the pages of this book that I offered a safe place for others to share their gratitude stories out loud. The journey has been incredible. The amazing humans that have shared their stories with us here are all radiant examples of gratitude in action.

The stories that follow are directly from the authors, who bravely chose to share their experiences. This book is not heavily edited. Each author has a unique voice, and I wanted to honor this. As I was collecting and arranging them, I felt so much love, joy, honor, compassion and hope. In a world that is full of "busy"ness and fake news, this book is a quiet respite. I invite you to create a quiet space, perhaps grab a cup of warm tea or a glass of wine and enjoy the magic that unfolds amongst the following pages.

Deeply Grateful,
Alexsys

P.S.
Moved to share your gratitude story? There will be other books in the Gratitude 540 series and I would love you to consider expressing your gratitude out loud in an upcoming book to submit a story for consideration: https://alexsysthompson.com/gratitude-series.

You are also welcome to join our Facebook Group called Trybal Sanctuary: https://www.facebook.com/groups/trybalsanctuary/.

There are also a few FAQ's at the end of this book to help you understand the title etc.

Daddy's Girl

by Kelly Potts

I count my blessings daily, and one of those blessings is my dad, Maurice George Ivers. I thank God He chose him to be my dad. A dad's job of raising a daughter cannot be an easy one. I know I caused him and my mom, Joyce (Pulleyblank) Ivers, a lot of stress and worry during my teenage years. However, looking back, he made parenting seem so easy.

I am extremely proud of him and will tell anyone who will listen. My dad served in the Marines in the Vietnam War. This is one of his proudest accomplishments. I take pride in being the daughter of a Marine Vietnam Veteran. My dad has and continues to give me nothing but the best advice and unconditional love.

When my dad returned from the Marines, he went to work on the family farm his father started and had worked on growing up. He still works on this farm today with great pride alongside his brother, son, and nephews. I spent a lot of time on the farm with my dad growing up. One of my greatest memories is mom taking me to the field to ride with my dad in the tractor. I would take a pillow and sleep on the floorboard of the tractor if I got sleepy, while hauling grain in the 10-wheel grain trucks, which have now been upgraded to several semis.

My love of country music, 50s music, and 60s music comes from my dad. He introduced me to Tanya Tucker's music and taught me to sing her song, "Delta Dawn"; which is still one of my favorite songs today. Maybe because he changed the words to be Kelly Dawn, my name.

When I was younger and would do something wrong, Dad remained calm when he would talk to me about what I had done. In fact, that's how I knew when I really screwed up, he wouldn't talk to me at all. I got the silent treatment until he was ready to discuss, calmly, what I had done wrong. I don't recall him ever raising his voice at me. Ever.

Like most teenagers, my driver's license did not come with a car. Nope, I wasn't spoiled in that way. For me, I got to drive my mom's mini-van at first. My first car didn't come along until 1986, I believe, and it was a 1977 Camaro that needed some work and a paint job; nothing too fancy. Lucky for me, my dad was an amazing mechanic! I remember him telling me one time, *"Now if you're going to race, you have to race for pink slips… and you better win."* For those of you that don't know what a pink slip is, it is the title to your car. Needless to say, I never did race for fear of losing my car.

Having that car did not come without its lessons. He taught me to change the oil, air filter, and tires and such. It was my responsibility to take care of it. He would help me and teach me, but I was to learn from this. Something I still carry with me today. Trust me when I say, my husband Sean is thankful for this. As a matter of fact, when Sean and I were dating, a cassette got stuck in my tape deck. It had happened before, and my dad had obviously shown me how to fix it. So, I pulled my car in the shop at the farm and started to pull the whole tape deck out, fixed it, put it all back together and off we went. Sean was floored! He asked me how I knew how to fix it. I just smiled and said, *"my daddy taught me."* If it were possible to teach common sense, well, he did that for me.

I have tried my best to pass on the values and morals that he and my mother raised me with to our two sons, Ryan and River Potts. I have told both boys the exact words he told me before starting high school. *"Enjoy these next four years because they will go by fast. I know you don't think they will, but they will, then you will get married and have kids, and they will go even faster."* He was so right! My husband and I also spend time alone doing things without our boys, because that was some more advice, I remember my dad giving me. He told me to always maintain common interest with my spouse and do not make my life all about my children. He said, *"They will grow up and they will leave you."*

The devotion and love my dad showed my mom while she was sick, and we were losing her to cancer, is untouchable. I can only pray that if I am ever in that position, I can be half as strong as he was for her and for our family.

I have never needed for anything. My dad taught me the value of a dollar and to work for it. Something that seems to be disappearing in parenting these days. My dad raised me to be independent, so I would not have to depend on a man to take care of me. He raised me to speak my mind and to be confident.

There are no words or actions I can say or do to ever express to him how grateful I am to have him as a dad. I can only hope he is proud of the daughter he had a hand in raising and knows that even if he thought I wasn't listening and paying attention, I was. I hope I am half the parent he has been, and I hope I make him proud.

Dedicated to my daddy. I hope this letter of gratitude helps him realize just what a wonderful man, dad, and grandpa he truly is! I love you Daddy!

Do You Always Smile?

by Jenny Austgen

It was a beautiful fall day when I was riding my mountain bike through the wooded areas of a small mountain summer retreat town in Japan. I had just arrived four weeks earlier and had begun the difficult task of learning the Japanese language and culture. I was in classes all day, so I wanted to go outside to get a little exercise before beginning my homework for the evening. That is when I came across an older American woman walking through the woods. She introduced herself to me and let me know that we both worked for the same non-profit organization. Then she turned and said, *"Do you always smile?"*. That was the beginning of a long friendship that I still cherish to this very day. Over time, I would come to call this woman my mentor, co-worker, mother, teacher, and dear friend. There were so many qualities that I admired in this lovely lady who was twice my age at the time. How did I come to give this woman, whose name is Ellen, all those different titles? Let me share with you a glimpse into the many reasons why.

I called her my hugging mom. I was far from home and was struggling with culture shock, and she reached out to me with open arms to welcome me into their home for many meals, games, and movie nights with popcorn. She and her husband had been living in Japan for over 20 years and had been dorm parents for teenage boys in a boarding school in Tokyo. Now their kids were grown, and they were living in a small mountain village running a coffee shop on conference grounds before retiring and returning to America. She always made it a point to welcome all the single ladies that came through the language school and treated each and every one as if they were her very own children.

I called her Miss Hospitality. It was my first Thanksgiving away from home and Ellen made it a point to invite every single person over to their home for a homemade meal and a time to share what we were thankful for. It was one of the best holiday meals I had ever had. Afterwards, we all went hiking up the mountain to make room for pie. And of course, everything was made from scratch! I think I counted 26 people for dinner. The kindness I felt that day will always be etched on my heart as a reminder of the importance of being there to encourage others on their journey. In the fourteen years I spent in Japan, I saw many people come through this home. Some people were Japanese, some Canadian, some German, and some American. All were shown the same love, and all were extended a hand of kindness, which usually also included receiving a plate of her homemade cinnamon rolls that were fresh out of the oven and still warm. It was her way of saying God loves you and so do I.

I called her my mentor. There were so many important lessons I learned from her that impacted my life for the good. She was so organized that she would plan out her whole summer meal calendar. I guess the reason for this was because they usually had guests in their home visiting and helping out at the conference center, and she didn't have time to make multiple trips to the grocery store. She also would do what she could the day before, so she wouldn't be stressed out when company arrived. I would often come over and help her set the table the night before and do preparations in advance since I lived close by. I learned quickly, and after a time she challenged me to become the cultural host on Sundays and teach her guests how to make different Japanese meals during their visits.

I called her co-worker because we both worked for the same non-profit organization. We ran English conversation camps together for Japanese young people. Together, we planned events for the young adults in a nearby Japanese church. I also helped out in their coffee shop when large groups would come to the conference center. I will never forget the time we sponsored and took a group of Japanese to the States to attend a convention on the West Coast. Ellen had every detail of the trip planned. This included shopping, of course, which was a necessity for the Japanese in order to bring something back for those who couldn't go on the trip. Ellen showed me the importance of detail. She was the person you wanted on your team because you knew that nothing would ever be overlooked.

I called her teacher because she taught me how to make many crafts with my hands. I learned how to cross stitch, quilt, paint on wood, and use Japanese Washi paper in crafts. But the greatest thing I learned from her was the lesson of perseverance. In all that she did over the many years that we worked together, she never once complained. She would never show it, but underneath her smile, she was dealing with a disease called Ankylosing Spondylitis. Some days it would get the best of her. Her "hang in there" spirit is summed up in this vivid picture that I will never forget. On a day when she could barely walk down the hall with the aid of crutches, she was dragging the bathroom garbage can down the hall with one of her crutches in it. With a laugh and a cracked smile, she taught me how to never give up.

And last, I call her my dear friend. It has been many years since we both lived in the same mountain village of Japan, but we still talk on the phone from time to time. I am grateful for the many memories that we shared over the years. In this journey called life, sometimes we just need someone to show us the dance of life. Sometimes we need someone to remind us of God's goodness no matter where the journey might take us.

Dedicated to Ellen Bardeau
Thank you, Ellen for teaching me how
to love God and others.

Grandma's Hands

by Dane Vannatter

In a file cabinet, in my apartment, is a blue pocket folder. Inside that folder are copies of various documents pertaining to my grandmother's life before I knew her. That blue folder goes with me, everywhere I go. Memories of my grandmother, for the 9 years I knew her, will live in my heart and mind forever. I acknowledge, and regret, that many of the questions I have about her earlier life may never be answered, but I keep searching.

Grandma's hands clapped in church on Sunday mornings. They strummed guitars, played piano, and wrote songs. Grandma's hands sewed simple cotton dresses, drove big clunky Chevys, trimmed back rose bushes, gave comfort, and baked pies. And until she died, when I was 9-years-old, Grandma's hands were always available to me.

My parents both worked, so I was shuttled to Grandma's house a lot. She took me to church with her on Sundays, where I first learned how much I loved to sing. She taught me where middle C was on her piano. We sang from church hymnals, songs like *"The Pilot's Hand on Mine"* and *"I Want to be a Hero for the Lord."*

When I was 8 years old, we recorded a stack of songs she had written into a tiny reel to reel tape player that was set on a chair next to my end of the piano bench. My high clear boy soprano voice sang *"I Was Born to Serve the Lord."* Grandma harmonized with me on a song she had written years before with her husband, Charles Edward Vannatter, the grandfather I never knew. He died of a heart attack almost 10 years before I was born. Their song was called *"I'm on My Way to Glory."*

Grandma's hands were lined with thick bluish veins. They looked like deep rivers coursing thru liver spotted canyons. With my fat pudgy fingers, I would press down on those veins until the rivers seemed to stop flowing, then I'd stop pressing and watch the veins fill up again. Grandma didn't own a television, so we played music and sang songs instead. Grandma time was always play time for me.

When I was 7, I fell out of our backyard apple tree and broke my left arm. That evening, Grandma placed her hands on me and prayed and my arm stopped aching. Grandma's hands issued out love and acceptance. I felt it deeply when I was a child. I trusted Grandma. She would even let me dress up like a girl and run around her house carrying one of her old purses; those big boxy purses of hers that were always filled with combs and pens and tissues along with her church notes and song lists from revival meetings. I loved her so much. It seems like she was always smiling, always gentle and always soft-spoken. It never occurred to me that she had a life before us… before me.

Her name was Elizabeth Ivy Brooks Vannatter, and she was born in 1892. Grandma told me that she was raised on a farm with many brothers and sisters. She found her bond to religion one day when one of the farm horses cornered her against a fence and began to rear. The young Elizabeth closed her eyes and prayed, and the horse walked away.

I knew that she was very involved in her family's church and that later somewhere along the line she converted to the Church of God and divorced her first husband because he drank too much. I'm not sure where she met my grandfather, but they both became ministers of their church in Plymouth, Indiana. My blue pocket folder is filled with songs they wrote together and poems they wrote to each other. They also brought their ministry and music to prisons and jails. I'm not sure why they focused on death row inmates in particular, but I suspect they had a profound respect for the sixth commandment, "Thou Shalt Not Kill."

At home in our family bookcase, there was a small stack of old brown envelopes that contained handwritten letters on prison stationery from the Central Prison of Raleigh, North Carolina. My grandparents had temporarily relocated from Indiana to North Carolina in the mid 1930s. I was fascinated by the letters, but I never discussed them with my grandmother. At the top of each letter, the mast read *"Send your relative or friend: books, magazines, fruit, candy, toilet articles, money, cigarettes, and tobacco. Do not send: stamps, pencils, pens, stationery, medicine, and clothing. "A" Grade men write once a week, "B" grade men write twice a month. "C" grade men write once a month."* Then: *"Please write cheerful letters."*

These were death row inmates, men whose souls my grandparents hoped to save by singing for them and supplying them with bibles and Christian newsletters. All of my grandmother's letters were from "C" grade men, so many of these letters were the last letters they would ever write. The next day would be their execution day. I remember how the intimacy of these letters made me feel strange and I couldn't fathom how anyone could feel ready to die. But I knew my grandparents had done something good and that they were a blessing to these men.

My folder of Grandma's songs, poems, diaries, and prison letters is barely 3 inches wide. However, my memories of Grandma and how much she loved me is unquantifiable. That love is a force that still sees me through dark days, and her music has influenced my own music career. How fortunate and rare to have a glimpse into a life lived so passionately for others. Delivered with love from my grandma's hands.

She died when I was nine but remembering her love and acceptance has helped to lift me up many times in my life. Her deep religious faith and commitment to the Church was something I didn't understand as a child, but I shared the love she poured into her music. She had a piano, a guitar and a record player. She valued solitude and quiet prayer. She loved Thanksgiving dinners and she made a great mincemeat pie! Grandma was my first hero I suppose, and I'm proud to give her this small tribute. Her grace and dignity and the care she brought to her family and to her community make me proud to be her grandson.

I dedicate this story to my grandmother,
Elizabeth Vannatter. Her convictions were strong,
her manner was tender, and she was the most
loving person I have ever known.

Breaking a Cycle, Making a Cycle

by Michele Palazzolo

My husband George and I both experienced very dysfunctional family lives growing up. Dysfunctional enough to form low expectations of relationships, to have low self-esteem and to anticipate continuing life as we had experienced it. In truth, we were able to rise above it and even gather strength from it.

George, who was 19 when we met, was in the middle of some extreme family drama at that time, however he exuded a sense of strength and compassion, and of composure and understanding. He was fascinating to me as he never used his current or past situations to define him or his potential. Within a year we were married, both of us very young and our life's path undefined. With the potential to repeat all that we had learned about families and relationships, we strived to be the opposite of it all. George continued to grow into an amazing man who is gentle, understanding and respectful. As a husband, he is all in on the relationship and never wavers, even if times are challenging. He displays more love for me than any one person deserves, it is unconditional, never hesitant and always endless. As a person from a comparative background this overwhelming acceptance, understanding, and patience lifts my soul to a place that is peaceful and trusting. His love breathes life into my existence and creates a feeling of unified strength that together we can conquer whatever we are faced with. We have through the years faced many issues and life challenges and although the stress and pressure from some of them can feel like more than any one person can endure, together, and with his strength and love, we continue to survive and somehow become stronger and closer through it all.

Early in our marriage, God blessed us with two amazing gifts... our sons. New lives that needed to be nurtured and developed in ways unfamiliar to us, ways different from what we had experienced ourselves. George was so touched, so inspired, so gentle, so loving. Watching him develop into a father was one of the most amazing experiences in my life. He was so selfless and always put the children first, it was almost as if you could visibly see his love for his children. He was amazing with the boys as he taught them to be the person he had grown to be; the person he knew he could be. They learned the real value of family and that family loves unconditionally and is always there when you need them. He taught them to be caring and respectful, he taught them to be responsible and accountable. I could have never imagined him being a better father than he was. He embodied every dream I had ever had of what I wanted the father of my children to be. To this day our now adult children know the love and support they have in this family, and they represent the core values that George so deeply believes in. George has been instrumental in crafting a practical and functional expectation for our boy's future lives and relationships. Both boys are committed and are now replicating the lives they experienced early on with their own families. Both our sons are becoming the man their father is.

George does not limit his giant heart to just family, friends are extremely valuable to him as well. He embraces his friends with the same respect and kindness that he shows his family, he is caring and devoted to any and all. George will be the protector for ones in need, the shoulder for strength, and the confidant when needed. He does not shy away when times are tough, he embraces the situation, determines the need, and reacts with what best supports and assists in coping. This has been the case through life experiences and most recently through death experiences. While friends are coping with terminally ill family members and all that it entails, George has been there every step of the way doing everything he can to ease the burden. He has a gentle way about him that lets people know that they are special and that his caring is genuine. George's friends have a connection that will last their lifetime.

George is a survivor, he has never played the victim role or blamed anyone other than himself for any shortcomings and has never allowed his past to interfere with achieving his visions. Our life has not always been rainbows and unicorns, there have been hard times, there have been trying times, but we try to maintain focus on the important issues and always listen to our hearts.

George and I will be celebrating our fortieth wedding anniversary this year and anyone who knows where we came from realizes what an accomplishment that is.

With George, what you see is what you get, he does not pretend to be anything he is not, and he is as honest as they come. At the same time, he is witty and funny and makes people smile. Characters like George only come around every once in a while, and anyone who has the opportunity to have George in their lives is truly blessed.

For my husband George Palazzolo who makes
me feel safe and warm and with whom I enjoy
life with every day. You are my best friend
and my hero in life and in love.
I will always love you.

He Chose Us!

by Kelsie Williams

When I was 4 years old, I gained an extra parent who made our family whole at home again. When my mom added Wayne, my stepfather, to the crazy mix that was our family, I was able to see what a solid family foundation was because he cared for all four of us and my mom when he didn't have to. A stepparent is someone who chooses to love and raise someone else's child even though they aren't obligated to do so. A stepparent makes incredible sacrifices when they marry someone with children, and they know those children may never know the grand sacrifices they make for them, and yet they still do it.

Growing up, I had three parents: Mom, Dad, and Wayne. I lived with my mom and Wayne and saw my dad whenever I wanted. Wayne didn't have any kids of his own, he gave that up when he married my mom. He told her that her four kids were enough. We are still his family, even though him and my mom split up my freshman year of high school. After their divorce, he could've taken that moment and walked away and never looked back, he didn't. He never turned his back on us. He continued to love us, even more. Oh, he may have hollered at us and threatened to take everything fun away at times, but never did he wipe his hands clean and walk away. He continued to love us unconditionally.

I have a lot of memories growing up with my stepdad. Like when I was about 4 or 5 years old, and he would brush my hair as I sat on the floor in front of him in his big burgundy recliner at his house. Or how he taught me how to ride the bike he and my mom bought me for my 5th birthday, after throwing me a big party with my friends at Discovery Zone. I remember how school grades were a big thing in our house. Wayne would pay us $5 for every 'A' we got on our report cards, and $2 for every 'B', and if you made straight 'A's you would get to choose a place to go eat dinner and then afterwards do something fun. I remember choosing a go-kart place one time. I still remember how fun that night was. In high school, I was very active in dance and other extracurricular activities, and when my mom couldn't get me to and from practices, it was Wayne who did. Throughout my childhood, and as an adult, my stepfather did everything a father does for their own child. There are so many memories I could mention here that showed me what being a parent to someone else's child should be. I had no idea then, that he was laying the foundation for me later in life when I would become a stepparent.

During my freshman year of high school, my mom and Wayne split up. And to no one's surprise, he never ever once changed how he treated and cared for us kids after their divorce. He was always there to get us where we needed to go, if we didn't have a ride, and he was always there to give us $5 for every 'A' on our report cards. When the time came to buy my first car, he called me to offer to help and I never even had to ask. Our parents didn't buy us cars, so I decided to save up and buy my own. I had almost enough but was a little short so Wayne paid the rest and I made payments to him every month until the car was paid off. I paid for all but $1,000 of that car because that was a gift from Wayne to help me out! I was ecstatic! I would go pick him up at his place and he always went with me to get my oil changed and sometimes my car washed. We spent Christmases with him at his place with just us kids and him, and he never missed important events. When I got married, he walked down the aisle as one of my parents and sat in the front row with my mom and dad.

A couple of years later things went south in my life and I went through a divorce. He called me regularly and even asked if I needed to stay with him for a little while. I felt like a failure, but he constantly assured me that I wasn't, and he promised to always have my back. He told me how proud he was of me and how proud he'd always been of me. I wish I could explain how much just knowing I had him in my life, helped me push through all the drama during that time.

It wasn't long before I met and fell in love with the man I'm married to now, and he had a very young son at the time. Sometimes I questioned whether or not I was doing the right thing at such a young age by taking on the responsibility of being a stepparent and whether or not I could be a good role model for his little boy. I prayed long and hard asking if this is what God had planned for me. I often worried what would happen if things didn't work out and my heart was invested in this child, but then I always thought about Wayne. I knew that as long as I loved this little boy the way Wayne loved me and my brothers and sister, then everything would be fine. Wayne undoubtedly provided me with the right "tools" to be the best stepparent I could be for my stepson. My plan was to be just like Wayne. He quickly became my biggest role model.

It wasn't until I got older that I understood the sacrifices he gave up being our father. He gave up having his own children when HE CHOSE US, and he never looked back. He loved us unconditionally from day one. He could've walked away and said the package was just too big. But he didn't. When I got older it really sank in that I wasn't just one of Wayne's stepdaughters, I was one of his daughters. He treated us as if we were his own blood family, and he still does. He was a father to us growing up, he is a father to us now, and he is a proud and loving grandfather to our children. If it weren't for Wayne, I don't know that I would've had the courage to marry a man with a child. I don't know that I would've realized how lucky I was that someone wanted me to love their child as Wayne has always loved us. I know that I would not be living this amazing life I live today with my husband, my stepson and our 2 other children, if I never had Wayne as a parent in my life from such a young age. And for that, I am grateful!

To my bonus dad, Wayne Campbell, thank you
for CHOOSING us. I wouldn't be the parent or
stepparent I am today if you hadn't walked into
our lives so many years ago. Thank you for
being my real-life hero! I love you so big!

Body of Work

by Jonti Bolles

By most definitions, a Body of Work typically refers to an artist and their contributions to a collection created over time.

I am grateful for a man in my life, Richard B. Ferrier, FAIA, 1944 – 2010 for teaching me the true meaning and value of a Body of Work. Richard was a registered architect, successful artist, singer, and Fellow of the American Institute of Architects.

I was a graduate student at UTA in the School of Architecture. At the end of my first year of Grad school I interviewed with Richard, who was the Assistant Dean, to talk about becoming a graduate teaching assistant (GTA). I didn't have much confidence at the time but wanted desperately to succeed and continue my path. Other than a large intro lecture class with hundreds of other students, this was my first real interaction with Richard. He quietly asked questions, looked me in the eyes, and said he would do what he could to find any matching opportunities.

It was humbling to ask for help. A few weeks later, I was notified there would be a position for me during the

Fall semester. It wasn't much but allowed me to stand on my own two feet and stay in graduate school. His act of kindness was honest and part of why he was the Assistant Dean. Teaching that first semester with an experienced professor brought me more joy and confidence than I imagined.

The summer before I was to begin teaching as a graduate assistant, Richard was teaching a popular class on the Indian ruins in Northern New Mexico. Although I really wanted to take the class and explore both art and architecture, it was full. While I wasn't projecting much confidence in my life at the time, Richard saw something others didn't. As my personal life hit some solid walls, Richard picked up on the focus that Graduate school was providing me at the time. He allowed my registration in the class, and we become mentor and student on that trip and subsequent projects. It began a story of respect and friendship that lasted beyond the studio. I would later work part-time with Richard in his practice. I became friends with his studio partners, and we often took trips to New Mexico or around Texas for jaunts including fly-fishing, painting, and architectural planning.

Upon graduation, I was ready to start my Architectural career, but not before a semester in Italy that Richard supported by writing a recommendation letter for a partial scholarship. While I was out of the country, Richard had started consulting with an HBCU Architectural program in the Houston area. They were rebuilding the program and needed to bring on an additional professor. Upon my return to the States, Richard suggested I apply for the position. He stressed this was a place I could make a difference and my balance of knowledge, sense of fairness, and my fascination with technology would serve all very well. Richard was tireless and traveled from Dallas to Houston weekly for several years to consult, teach, and help guide the program. I often picked him up at the airport, driving to the university, and we planned new projects and programs over late-night dinners and drawing boards. It became the beautiful story of seven years teaching at a school that we watched grow, achieve accreditation, and produce better-prepared students. His example helped change the face of the industry by bringing more minorities into the architectural field. The fulfillment we received was one we gladly shared and we were proud of our contributions.

Years later, we both ended our time at the HBCU knowing it would continue to grow with strong foundations. Weeks, months, and a few years passed with a friendly note to one another, a sketch on a postcard, or a phone call every now and then. The time in between contact stretched longer, for no reason other than distance and taking for granted the comfortableness of our friendship.

I received a phone call with news about Richard's passing. After moments of disbelief, I settled into focusing on the precious gift I had been given of his friendship. I made plans to travel to the memorial with a common friend and we shared stories and memories along the half-day drive across Texas.

At the memorial, I renewed friendships with others who were also touched by Richard's friendship, kindness, and support. I listened to stories like mine of how Richard had quietly helped them with a decision around a class, encouraged them to enter a drawing competition, wrote a letter of recommendation, and countless other large and small acts of support. Each person had their own personal story that was unique and a powerful pivot point in their life. Richard had no gain in each of these stories, just the satisfaction of helping others.

While Richard was characterized as an artist with stereotypical artist habits, his charisma and talent allowed him to move beyond the traditional and into realms of creativity with song, art, and architecture that reflected what he saw in life and society.

As I walked the architecture building and gallery during Richards' memorial with his artwork curated, you could see the development of his art over time and how different periods were reflected on paper and canvas. I met person after person that came to pay their respects and share stories just as I had. That's when I stepped back and could see the real breadth and legacy of his work.

What he created in his life was so much more than objects and art, it was the incredible reach of single acts of kindness and faith that continue to spread and touch others. His portfolio or "Body of Work" was the count-less stories and acts of service compounded. Each act provided an opportunity for someone to grow and be in a position to do the same for someone else. Each story in the portfolio was beautiful on its own. Collectively, the portfolio of stories was stunning, and I was so thankful to see the accumulation of a lifetime of work.

To have the privilege of hearing so many stories at once, to understand how my own life fit in a chapter was humbling. It inspired me to continue the legacy of help-ing others without any expectation of their repayment, success, or gratitude. Richard saw beyond what people asked for and tried to provide opportunities for what they needed. My mission is to someday have such a rich Body of Work as my legacy and I am so grateful to the artist that showed us by example what creating something beautiful truly means.

Richard, I owe you my gratitude for being
a friend, mentor, giving of your time,
and being a gentle teacher. Thank you.

The Healing Power of 13 Words

by Chanelle Carlin

On September 17, 2017, my mom Michele Marguerite Hollinger passed away at the age of 67. This story is my thank you note to her.

Barely more than a child herself, my teenage mom poured all her love and adoration into her babies, hoping we would always be there to love her. I never doubted that she loved me and my brother more than life itself, but even as a child, I felt she held me responsible for her life's fulfillment. I felt smothered and overly burdened with responsibility...responsibility to care for my brother, to care for her, to be the perfect daughter and granddaughter. I was supposed to go to college, have a great career, and be the perfect mommy. While my brother got to be a kid and even get into trouble, I never did. I had to be responsible.

As I got older, her need to live vicariously through me increased and as a result, I felt an increasing need for air and space. I had to break free. When I was 19, I moved out with a girlfriend. When I was 21, I moved to

Los Angeles and didn't tell her until the day before my flight left. When I was 31, I moved to Ireland, where I finally felt free to be just me and where I experienced eight amazing years of freedom. I moved back home in 2007 and just a short time later, I was back to being responsible.

The symptoms were mild at first. She was unable to count her points when she played Rummy (a card game), and was scared to be on her own when she had lived on her own for years. We pushed aside our worries believing the symptoms were related to the stress of her job and later the lack of a job. When we finally convinced her to see her doctor, she was misdiagnosed and treated for clinical depression. Unfortunately, her symptoms worsened dramatically and in 2012, a year and a half later and through my brother's persistent advocacy (she lived with him at the time), she was diagnosed with moderate-severe dementia. A short time before her diagnosis, she gave my brother and me power of attorney over her care and finances. She trusted no one else…she had no one but us.

Over the next five years, her condition worsened as it does with this disease. She stopped recognizing her grandchildren first. Eventually, she began calling me "Mom" and introducing me to everyone as "my mommy". She was always glad to see me come and sad to see me leave.

This brings me to the 13 healing words. The last time my mom was really mobile and we were able to enjoy time together outside was about a month before she died. It was a beautiful sunny day. I arrived in the morning, we spent time doing what we usually did: talking, walking and chatting with the ladies she lived with at the Memory Care residence. After lunch, we went outside and sat on a bench in the courtyard surrounded by lovely flowers, green grass, and chirping birds. There was a soft breeze blowing. We talked some more and then she napped. While she was napping, I sat next to her and wrote a letter to a friend in Ireland. It was a beautiful day in all ways. As I drove the seven hours back home, I had a sense that things were changing, but mostly I just enjoyed the wonderful visit. The next day, I called on the telephone and talked to her as I did every day. During this call, I could hear a difference. It wasn't the little girl who thought of me as her "mommy", but my Mom, Michele. I seized the moment and asked her if she knew who I was. Her words ring as clear to me now as they did then and still bring the same tears of joy to my eyes. For the first time in years, she said to me, *"Of course, I know you. You're my daughter, Chanelle and I love you."*

That was the last phone conversation I got to have with my mom and at about 10:30 pm on September 16, 2017, I said goodbye to her for the last time. I bent down next to her with my lips right next to her forehead while I stroked her hair. I told her that I was going to get a little sleep and that I would see her in the morning. I then thanked her for being a wonderful Mom, for loving us unconditionally and for doing such a great job raising two kids by herself. I reminded her of her six beautiful grandchildren. I also told her that while I would be back in a few hours, I knew she was really tired and that if she was too tired to wait for me and wanted to go, that it was alright. We would be alright and take care of each other. We loved her. I loved her. She hadn't spoken for days, but as I told her I loved her for the last time, she whispered, *"I love you."* In that second, I knew that was all that mattered then…all that matters now…it's all that ever matters.

Thank you, Mom, thank you for making me responsible and for giving me the gifts of love, strength, memory and of understanding what's most important. Thank you for giving me the courage to follow my dreams even when you didn't really want me to. Thank you for the gift of healing. I love you.

For my mom, Michele Marguerite Hollinger, who allowed me to heal our hearts with a lifetime's worth of love in one simple sentence.

Br. Anthony Rex Norris I Am Grateful For You

by Amy Poulin

Five years ago it didn't occur to me that the spiritual director my faith needed so desperately would become one of my dearest friends. There isn't a day that passes that I don't feel gratitude for Br. Rex, and the beauty he has helped me find in my relationship with God. I can remember the first question he asked me at our first meeting as well as my answer. Why did I need spiritual direction? Well, because I didn't need a counselor, I needed someone to help me grow in my faith. I wanted a friendship with God. He has done exactly that in more ways than he will take credit for.

"People drive me crazy Br. Rex!" Boy is that a phrase that has brought about more self-knowledge than I think I wanted. He calls them saint makers. How many times has Br Rex said, *"We are all trying to be saints, what else is there?"* Now that makes perfect sense to me however it didn't make sense that I would be someone's saint maker. You know those people who cut you off in traffic or take

forever to tell you a story, the people that make you roll
your eyes simply because they are coming towards you?
Well I have learned there are people who don't like driving behind me, those who don't appreciate my humor
when storytelling, and there are people who probably
don't appreciate seeing me coming either. I have learned
through Br. Rex and his example of humility that God
doesn't love me more than He loves anyone else, He
already loves me as much as He's ever going to, it's not
a contest. I had never thought of it that way. My whole
purpose in my faith life was to show God how much I
loved Him by doing acts of service that would prove to
Him how much I loved Him. I thought that's what I
was supposed to do. Br. Rex has taught me to look at the
phrase "Practicing Catholic" more seriously. Br. Rex is a
consecrated hermit who lives his life centered in Christ,
in sacred silence, solitude, and intercessory prayer. He is
always practicing being a better follower of Christ and he
has mirrored that to me. Not only do I want to be Christ-
like, but I want to be Br. Rex-like too.

Each time we have the opportunity to sit together
to pray and to talk it's a true blessing to me. In our first
meetings, it was Br. Rex, me and his sweet little cat,
Clare. The more we met, the more I realized that this
friendship and his guidance brought about a third presence, well fourth if you count Clare, and that presence is
Jesus. Whenever I would refer to the "something" that
brought happiness or understanding or clarity to a situation I'd say I didn't know what "it" was. Then boom, it hit
me. The Holy Spirit was the "it". I will forever be grateful
for Br. Rex bringing that to me. He is wise beyond mea-
sure. He has brought me deeper into my faith by guiding

and nurturing, not by telling me this is what you should think, and this is why you should think it. He cheers me on when I share with him that I recognized a song lyric that comes directly from the Bible. He wants to see my faith grow as much as I do. I have asked what I think are some really stupid questions and he's never laughed at me. He has a wonderful laugh, but he reserves it for humor and not my questions. I am grateful for that.

I refer to him as a champion prayer which is something I want to be. How does one even define what a champion prayer is? I wanted to be authentic and genuine when asked to pray for someone, but I was often overwhelmed with keeping it all straight. What if I forgot someone, what if I forgot what they wanted me to pray for? I couldn't imagine how Br. Rex kept all that intercessory prayer straight but I knew I wanted him to help me figure it all out. When I ask him to pray for a special intention he will always say *"I'm happy to join you in prayer"*. That makes such obvious sense to me now. If I'm asked to pray for someone or something why shouldn't it be in unison with the requestor? He has taught me to be intentional and honest. He is a champion prayer. His suggestion of tucking all intentions in my heart and then giving "all the intentions in my heart" to God has helped me to be a better champion prayer. I'm not perfect, something Br. Rex reminds me is an honor reserved for God alone but I am practicing and I will continue to practice with one of the dearest friends I've ever had.

Br. Rex was recommended to me when I began seeking a Spiritual Director and I recommend him to others now as well. That is how I know he has not only become my friend, he is the friend to many. I feel immense gratitude that our personalities clicked at that first meeting so many years ago and that my journey includes him and his friendship.

When he is told how appreciated and adored he is, his response is always, *"Adoration is for God alone, but I appreciate what you mean and I'm grateful the Holy Spirit uses me to share Him with you"*. My Spiritual Director has brought me the friendship I wanted with God and God has brought me a friendship I don't ever want to be without.

> For Br. Rex. You have shown Him to me in the
> sunrise. I know when He meets you face to face,
> He will say well done my good and faithful son.
> I'm grateful for you and your friendship. My life
> is better because of your example of faith.

Ode to Dad

by Linda Bush

Dear Dad,

You have been gone many more years than I ever knew you personally, but I am amazed how often I think of you and how much your influence has impacted my life.

In your fifty-eight earthly years, you overcame obstacles and setbacks, yet you carried yourself with dignity and grace. You passed on pearls of wisdom to me while sharing the simple elements of life that brought you joy and pleasure.

You treasured music and were quite a talented dancer. I loved watching you dance with mom and witness the love you felt for each other, overshadowing the times that life's challenges created tension between you. Our console stereo was your most prized possession which led to magical Sunday afternoons when we pushed away the furniture and danced ballroom and soft shoe style to the classics of Ella Fitzgerald, Frank Sinatra and more. These experiences created my love for dance and desire to explore a multitude of dance styles in high school and college, and in my adult life such as ballroom, modern dance, swing, jitterbug, and country line dancing. When I revealed my dream to join the 5th grade choir you made sure I attended every extracurricular rehearsal and never missed a performance. By the way, both of my children inherited your musical abilities. Your grandson Jason was a very talented trombone player, and your granddaughter, Suzanne, not only excelled on the snare drum but inherited your love and talent for dance.

You were not demonstrative with your faith but ensured I received a strong Christian education as a basis for my life's decisions. Your own father's early death shortened your formal education. This seemed to create a fire in your gut to learn all you could while continuously challenging me with word and number games at the dinner table. You also constantly reminded me and encouraged me to strive to attend college, which I did, and became one of the first in our family.

You were a southern boy and with a mischievous twinkle in your eye shared many jokes that today would not be acceptable. Yet there was not a mean bone in your body and you would go out of your way to help anyone regardless of race or pedigree. You demanded that I behave with dignity and class and always insisted I offer to lend a helping hand to everyone regardless of their circumstances. You passed to me your enjoyment of people and friends and your love of life.

Your favorite sport was baseball and you were known for your passion for our local team, the Houston Colts, who became the Houston Astros. You introduced me to baseball when I was age six by taking me to see the opening of the Houston Colt Stadium. With you dressed in your sport coat and tie, and myself in a spring dress, you patiently explained the rules of the game while supplying me with my fill of hotdogs and chocolate ice cream, hoping to instill that love of the game experience. You frequently attended the afternoon "business man special" games with your work buddies. The game was always on the radio at every family picnic by the San Jacinto River. You would go to great lengths never to miss a play, even keeping an old transistor radio to your ear as you ran from your car into the house to turn on the radio. I wish so much you had been here to witness the Astros finally achieving in 2017 every fan's dream – winning the World Series! By the way Dad, your "baseball loving" genes were quite evident in your grandson, Jason, who attended Astros games at Minute Maid Park at every opportunity.

I, on the other hand, inherited your enjoyment of football, and fondly recall our one-on-one outings to the Houston Oilers games. Sadly, many years after you passed, the Houston Oilers franchise departed Houston. By then I had achieved your dream of graduating college and thus directed my football enthusiasm to my alma mater, the University of Houston Cougars, which I still enjoy and share with my husband.

Dad, I was blessed with your loving presence for only fifteen years, but for the last forty-nine years, I have felt your presence and influence. Our life was simple and modest, but you raised me with southern manners, dignity, and a whole lot of Texas pride in being a direct descendent from the Republic of Texas and of David Catchings Dickson, Lt Governor of Texas, 1853-55. I, too, believe that, next to heaven, Texas is the greatest place to live.

Speaking of heaven, dad, I hope that your grandson Jason found his way to you and mom and that it was a joyous reunion as you got to meet him for the first time. I envision y'all enjoying lengthy baseball discussions with each other until my time comes to join you.

Love you Daddy,
Linda Jo

Dedicated to my dad, David Dickson Cook, for showing me how to live and love life to the fullest.

You Are My True Hero

by Amber Dowling

Memorial Day weekend 2015 is a weekend I will never forget. My son, Hudson was around eight months old when he began to have Infantile Spasms (a type of seizure). He was immediately taken to a neurologist in Dallas where they started injections twice daily in hopes that the seizures would stop. I prayed and prayed that God would heal my baby. At first, the neurologist gave us little hope that Hudson would ever walk or talk. However, further testing came back normal.

The medication that he was given seemed to work and eventually, we weaned him off and thought we were on our way to living a normal life. One week shy of his first birthday, Hudson had a relapse. I remember standing by his crib crying, thinking this can't be happening again. This time the outlook wasn't good. The neurologist said that my son would have trouble learning to walk, talk, and other learning milestones. I wasn't willing to accept that fate for him, I needed more answers.

Being from Houston, I knew how amazing Texas Children's Hospital was and I knew that's where Hudson needed to be. Six months passed by when we finally met with a neurologist from Texas Children's who thought something else was going on and immediately ordered more testing. One of the tests she ordered was called Whole Exome Sequencing, this would look further into the detail of Hudson's DNA. I was told that there was only a 33.3% chance of getting a diagnosis, and although I was scared, I was also anxious for answers. I waited 2 ½ months for those results.

June 21, 2016, I got the phone call, HNRNPU. Those six letters were all I had. I began doing my homework, but nothing came up. It seemed there was no other case in the United States. Nothing. It turns out Hudson had a seizure disorder with a list of other disabilities that no doctor could guide me through. I broke down and cried in my car, for the first time, and although I was scared, I knew that God had a plan. I COULD do this, and I WOULD give Hudson the life he deserved. In that parking lot, in my car, through my tears, I began to accept what God gave to me.

I used to stare at this perfect little baby sleeping in his crib, wondering what life was going to be like for him, and for me. Was I going to have to take care of him for the rest of his life? What age level would he max out at and stop learning? How was I, as his mother, going to do this? But you know what? You know how I did it, and how I do it? FAITH. I pray that God guides me to do what is best for my son. I learned to be his advocate and did research to find a doctor willing to dig in and research what my son had/has.

Since then, I started a Facebook page that now has around 40 other HNRNPU children and even some adults. They might all have the diagnosis but are all so different in so many ways. HNRNPU is something that makes them stand out and I have learned that it is okay that my son is different.

Hudson has shown me not to take things in life for granted. Simple things, like walking, talking, a toddler that gets into things, a toddler that is always on the move, and even a toddler who can recognize his own mother's face when he sees it.

I used to look at Hudson and wonder if he knew who I was. Does he know I am his mom; does he know I love him? Then one day I came home, and I realized he did not know who I was. I walked in the door, and he kept looking at me like I was a stranger. I never knew that type of pain until that day. My question was answered, my son did not know I was his mommy. I knew then that he may never know who I am, and he may never be able to call me mommy or tell me he loves me. But I wiped my tears and told myself, it will all be okay, God has plans for us.

My son may never be able to do what other children do, and that's okay. He may not be able to tell me when something is wrong or tell me what is hurting, or what he wants, and that's okay too. He tries... so I keep trying too. I will always be his mommy. I will always be his advocate. I will always be his voice.

Hillary Scott sings a beautiful song and has amazing lyrics that I will live by;

I know you see me
I know you hear me, Lord
Your plans are for me
Goodness you have in store.

Here we are going on three years later and Hudson is still the best thing life has ever given to me. He is my hero, and he continues to show me what true strength and happiness is, daily. While times have been hard and I break down and cry in the shower where nobody can see, I know my faith will get us through this. Hudson started walking with assistance after his fourth birthday. PROGRESS! Hudson is able to sign more. PROGRESS! Hudson can feed himself fifty percent of the time now. PROGRESS! This little boy is on a mission to prove doctors wrong.

As a young parent, I notice people in public staring at us or making snide remarks when he has an outburst. I still get stressed and worry about what other people think, however, I will not let it stop us from wanting to live somewhat of a normal life. I do not see a lot of parents who take their special needs kids out in public, and I know why. It is hard. It is an hour just trying to get out the door, only to be somewhere for sometimes 15 minutes, or maybe an hour if you're lucky. My grandmother once told me, *"They are a child first before they are a child with a disability."* This is something that will always stick with me. They deserve to do kid things; we just need to meet them where they are; give them the best life they deserve. I may not know what the future has in store for us, but I'm going to enjoy the journey with my best friend, while we find out.

This little boy who loves music and playing the piano is going to change the world. He is going to shock us all. He is one of the happiest little boys I know, and I am so blessed I get to be his momma. Not too long ago, for the first time in my son's life, he laid his head on my shoulder before bed and I rocked him even longer because I didn't want that moment to end. People constantly tell me that he adores me, and they can tell just by how he looks at me. I say this… he is my true hero, and I'm honored God chose me to be his mommy.

For Hudson, a mother is a gift in its own but being your mother is something truly special. You have given me a purpose and I will do everything I can to keep faith alive and to keep advocating for you. I love you!

Being Seen, Heard, and Understood in a Glance

by Alexsys Thompson

It was like an electric shock through my whole nervous system. This moment in which all time stopped and everything shifted into a consciousness I had not known before. It was an awakening into a myriad of possibilities of the life I could live.

What was this moment, I hear you ask? What could have had such an impact, without any warning it would? It was the split-second soul filled connection to another soul that was undeniably known and understood. There were no words in this exchange, it was the pure energy exchange of a love so true and clear that it shattered everything. The soul that saw me, heard my inner dialogue, and understood me in this nanosecond in time was called Curt Liesveld.

I was in training to become a certified Strengthsfinder Coach. I had been using the Strengthsfinder tool for years and was just now formalizing my training. As I look back on this time, the certification was more how I got there, Curt was the why. I was sitting in the back of the room, my back to a wall so I could see everything, as usual, and under the illusion, I was seeing and not being seen, a skill I had acquired over my lifetime. Curt was at the front of the room and had my full attention. I knew he was the real deal. He knew his stuff, and the way he was connecting patterns and things together while unique to most, was so how I saw it all working together. I was taking copious notes and expanding some of the concepts and connections to noodle around with later. It was as if something internal was switched on that had been off.

I looked up from my notes and my life changed. Curt was still in the front of the room and it was as if all time, motion, everything stopped. We caught each other's gaze. He saw through all the walls, veils, and mirages I had built around myself. I felt an electrical charge at that moment that jump-started a spiritual system within me that was deeper within my being than I knew existed. Imagine being in a house where all the windows and doors had been locked and most of them boarded up. You knew a few ways in and out and were very comfortable with where everything was, even in the dark. Without warning all the boards on the windows fell away and the windows flew open letting in sunlight and fresh air from a sweet summer morning breeze. Your sense of smell and feeling are lit up like a tree on Christmas morning, it is beautiful and a bit overwhelming to the senses. As I am writing this, I can feel that very deep part of my soul alert and ready for more discovery. Seems this gift that Curt gave me is one that will keep on giving.

A month after I finished my certification, Curt and I exchanged an email correspondence where he gave me the gift of being seen through his eyes and the strength language. We had spoken about the shame that can come with some strengths while in certification, and I have a strength called command in my top 5. I had taken the assessment again (at this time the 7th time) in an effort to have the command strength drop below my top 5 as then it would not be on my name card. I was gloating about being successful in getting it to number 6, now no one could see it. I know you are laughing as you read this, so am I. Curt was grace in action and let me have my gloat and during a break gently approached me with his beautiful grin and shared a short story about a girl he loved who also shared the command strength and how yes at times it was well, bossy. However, he quickly moved on to all the brilliance of the strength and how he witnessed it adding so much value to their family and to their community. This special someone was his wife. Again, I felt open, vulnerable and seen by Curt. My eyes welled with tears and he continued to allow me that as well, not trying to erase them or dismiss them. His way of being with me was life changing and I committed to being my version of this grace I was experiencing. I shared that with him and his face lit up and he said, *"The world won't be ready for it, and do it anyway"*. So, I am.

A lot of the work I am now doing and the rapid growth I am experiencing has stemmed from this interaction. I have had many other teachers along the way, but as you know, there is nothing like the first. While Curt has passed from this realm, I talk to him often and seek his guidance when I feel the desire to hide. Our communication and connection transcend time, space and the need to be human. He is the gentle whisper, the spring in my garden and an angel I am so blessed to have to support me in ways I am not currently conscious of.

I am in a deep metamorphosis and part of that is redefining how I present my physical form to the world and this includes the clothes I wear. I support many amazing leaders in what we call corporate America and there is a spoken and unspoken expectation for what that should look like. I have conformed for many years and am shedding that conformity this month. I long to wear clothes that are from natural fibers, that flow and are feminine in newly defined ways. I tried a few pieces last summer and I love them, it feels like the compliments I receive when I am wearing them are for me and so I go bravely into this new way of showing up. Last weekend I purchased five more pieces and will be implementing them into my work wardrobe. When I was trying them on last weekend, I heard Curt whisper, *"They won't be ready, do it anyway."* It is just one more step of being vulnerable, aligning my humanness to the divinity that lives within and is the truest form of me.

It is with the fullest heart and deepest adoration that I
thank Curt for being available for me at a pivotal time
in my awakening. His strong assuredness, gentle nature
and unwavering commitment to be his best version
of himself created the environment for me to see my
reflection in him. We are all connected, the very
thread that binds Curt and I binds you and I. Thank
you for being here to take this story in and I hope
in some way you see your reflection within it.

The Tie That Binds

by Candice Johnson

Blood is thicker than water. Although a well-known phrase and used frequently, it is not necessarily accurate in my case. I have learned that a bond between people that is created by love and respect can many times be much stronger than one of blood. These types of bonds are the most special, as they are bound by choice, not by circumstance.

My life was forever changed by a man when I was seven years old, a man that I fondly refer to as Dad. Albeit a stranger in the beginning, not someone today I can imagine my life without. This man made a choice to take on the responsibility of raising three additional children, not in the sense of a step-parent but in the sense of one of his own. I shall be forever grateful to him for that. At a young age, I had no idea how his selfless choice would define who and what I am as an adult.

Raising children is by no means an easy task and trust me, my dad had his hands full, not just with the three children he took in as his own, but with seven in total and a few misguided friends of mine and my siblings along the way. We certainly presented him with challenges, some that I am not sure an average person could have handled, but for a hero like him, he always came out on the other end, making sure he helped my mom to weather our storms as well. I may not have always heeded his advice, but trust me, he was forever giving it with the preemptive of "You are going to do what you want, but this is what I think". Looking back now, there are many times that I did do what I wanted at the time but wish that I had listened a little more to his advice as I probably would have saved myself and him some grief and heartache.

My dad has always been such a patient soul, always listening intently before responding, making sure that we all felt heard and showing us that our voices mattered. I attribute my independence and confidence to this. Don't get me wrong, my dad also has a sense of humor that can shame most comedians. Asking my dad a question always results in two answers, the first, some kind of ridiculousness and the second, his true answer. His chuckling out of nowhere and when asked why, his response, "Sometimes I just think funny thoughts". This, I can say is where I get my sense of humor from. Although life can sometimes be hard and stressful, Dad always finds a way to see the light at the end of the tunnel and this is where I get my determination from.

There are many milestones for a person through the stages of life from a small child, to a young adult and into adulthood. Learning to ride a bike, learning to drive, graduation, marriage, the birth of my children; my dad stood beside me and guided me through all of these stages. Because of this, I have never respected anyone as much as I do him. I can only hope that one day, I can be thought of as half the person my dad is.

Now that I am an adult, a parent and a grandparent, I reflect back on my upbringing frequently. Always remembering the selflessness of my dad and how his family always came first. No matter how tired my dad was from a long day of work, he always made time for us, playing games, volleyball in the backyard, toting us to and from sports events, birthday parties, sleepovers or working on school projects, he never made us feel like we were an inconvenience. Weekends were always about the kids, trips to Lake Livingston where I learned to water ski and developed my passion for fishing, not much there but a piece of ground and a couple of tents, but oh the memories that were made. Poor dad never got a chance to get his pole wet because he was constantly fixing one of the kids' poles or taking a fish off the hook for us, but he never complained. Excursions to the park, hiking the trails and playing ball - Dad always made sure that we were entertained. His inventive ideas in the backyard included a tarp and a water hose to create a slip-n-slide, and eating watermelon and squeezing the seeds at each other,

As an adult, things in life have a different perspective. The moments I cherish from my childhood may have been taken for granted when I was young, but now, I would not trade them for the world. Watching my dad and how he interacts with my children and my grandchildren, it warms my heart. I am so thankful that they also have an opportunity to feel the love of my dad and to make memories with him that they will be able to carry throughout their lives.

Most importantly, I watch my dad and how he loves my mom. The love he has for her is so apparent, in the way he looks at her and the way he always makes sure her every want and needs are met. This is a special love, and because of it, I have my dad in my life. I thank God for my dad and for bringing him into our lives to fill a void like no one else possibly could have. This is what set the expectation for me as to what a marriage should be like.

There is no one in this world that I admire more than this selfless, loving, and most of all inspiring individual. My dad has always been my rock, supporting me throughout my life in all of my decisions, good and not so good. Holding me up when I waiver, picking me up when I fall and standing proudly by my side when I shine. Blood may have made me but his love molded me.

Thank you, Dad, for always loving me, even when I did not make it easy for you. Thank you for being the tie that binds our family together, you are truly a blessing.

Dedicated to Brent Pitre

Shine Like Truth

by Rebecca Thompson

It is my belief that every young person needs a mentor. An adult who listens with respect and lets you know that youth matter. This is incredibly important in a world where kids spend the bulk of their days indoors, behind computer screens instead of outside interacting with others. Young people need to know that they matter, and that what they have to contribute today counts - not just what they will grow up to be and do. Sometimes it feels like we aren't living for today. Life is busier, people are stressed, and schedules are overbooked. Especially the children. Families aren't making time to sit down regularly and eat meals together, and when they do, it is often rushed. We are out of practice. People are struggling to connect. This is when I miss my grandmother the most. She knew how to build community and grow its individual members. She knew how to stay in the present moment. She was *holding space* before it became a tag line for care. It just came naturally to her. She shined like truth in every possible way.

I grew up in a small town in southern Vermont. I was fortunate to live in a community where everybody knew your name - and was quite capable of using it if you weren't behaving yourself! Running around outside was not only safe, but expected, as the preferred place for a child to play and spend the day was out of doors. Playmates were a dime a dozen if you just looked up and down the street. Driveways were race tracks for big wheels, yards were stomping grounds for any variety of tackling ball games, and the boundaries for tag, spud and other group games could extend beyond the borders of an individual property. Families shared recipes, kept the neighborhood children in their sights, and organized community picnics to bring everyone together. It was a pleasant place to grow up and life was simple.

An additional highlight for me was having my grandmother right down the street. She lived next to the general store which meant that we could stop in and say hello on our regular walks to purchase milk and eggs for the family table. We could wave to her from the bus stop or pop in after school for a treat and some conversation. My earliest slumber party memories do not include classmates, they include my favorite blanket, homemade chocolate sauce on ice cream, and meaningful conversations with my grandmother. There was much laughter, and I always felt that what I had to say and think and share were relevant and appreciated. She was an incredibly good listener.

Our connection continued throughout the teenage years. Laughter was replaced by tears at times, but the support was consistent and on-going. In those awkward days when heartbreak, friendship woes and parental arguments were standard, my grandmother provided a safe space. I am grateful for her companionship. I am grateful that I had the opportunity to release my emotions, talk through my frustrations, and be distracted from the daily grind. She maintained a reality that I could handle, and she allowed me to be vulnerable. Self-acceptance started on her couch. We could spend a perfectly wonderful afternoon just sitting together, sometimes without saying a word. Her positivity gave me strength and an outlook that helped me navigate those tough years. She also gave me innumerable moments to look back on and laugh about, even now. Like the time she allowed her grandchildren to teach her how to ride a bike - something she had never learned to do - under great objection from her own children. How many grandmothers would do that? She was fearless, in the gentlest way possible.

When I headed off to college, she kept our bond by writing me a weekly letter. Every Tuesday, I would walk to my mailbox and take out her latest note. When I came home for a weekend, she would plan a special meal and catch-up evening. Just the two of us. Truthfully, it was a big reason I visited home.

In my junior year, a sociology professor broke us up into discussion groups and asked us to write down one of our lifelong goals. Many things came to mind, but I chose one that stood out and wrote it on my index card. I then listened intently as we went around the circle and my classmates shared their aspirations one by one; to own their own business, to travel the world, to retire early having accumulated significant wealth. Eventually it was my turn. I read my card. The boy sitting next to me immediately laughed, as though I had just made a great joke, and then he sat and waited for my "real answer". I made eye contact with him. His smile faded, replaced by disbelief. *"That's it? Don't you have any REAL goals? You must!"* he insisted. So, I filled my classmates in. Being an amazing grandmother *is* a real goal. The impact that I can have on other human beings is significant; powerful even. I can help them discover and reach their own goals. I can help them navigate their challenges and support them in their own self-discovery. I can love them unconditionally and make time for them to let them know that they matter. That they are important. That they can make a great impact on this world, and do their own, individual part in making this world a better place for others. I can remind them not to take themselves too seriously. To take responsibility for their actions and make amends when needed. To take risks, and try new things, no matter how old they are. I don't know if any of my classmates truly understood my goal, and some still gave me odd looks, but the professor gave me an approving nod on the way out and that was enough for me.

The truth is, my grandmother did all of those things. Not for recognition, and not to prove a point. She just did them because that was who she was. Period. She was the most genuine person I have ever known. There was a truth to her that just radiated. She was comfortable in her own skin. She never tried to be something more or different than who she was, and she expected the same from anyone who entered her humble home. She found the positive in every situation. I see a reflection of her in my thoughts and actions, and in the friends that I have chosen to hold dear. I have always tried to create a safe space for others to stop by for a visit and just be in the present. I do my best to emulate her in my daily life and with my own children. She is always with me, and for that I am truly grateful.

I wonder if the difficulties and challenges we face today could be alleviated with some quality time spent together. Where individuals have the chance to share their thoughts with others who just listen without judging, and respect what they have to say, even when it is of the opposite point of view.

Perhaps it's time for all of us to honor the role that grandmothers play in our lives.

I dedicate this story to my loving grandmother, Elizabeth Cassidy Rice, as well as to Jane Harding Gurney, Elizabeth Gadue, and the many, many other wonderful grandmother figures who guide us with laughter, truth and light. We are so blessed to have you all in our lives.

My Uncle

by Timothy Bammel

It started with ice cream in my baby bottle, so I have been told. My uncle has always been one of my favorite people. He has shown me what it is to be a gentleman. He is a man's man, he is tough, he is strong. His patience has been tested numerous times in his life and each time he shines with the peace and love that we all should be fortunate enough to have. He is a constant in my life and I do not take that lightly.

I am thankful for the wonderful experiences and memories he has given me. He was driving the boat the first time I popped out of the water on water skis. He was there the first time I skied down a mountain. I was lucky to be included on this ski trip with my uncle, my aunt and cousins. It was in his truck that I practiced driving, with the assistance of my cousin, while he tended to their horses. Maybe he does not know about that one. He was at birthday parties, holiday get-togethers, graduations and so many other events throughout my life. He was there when I got married. In every memory I have of him, he is always smiling and enjoying himself. I am happy that I get to spend time with him.

He is generous with his time to everyone who knows him. He is who you call when you need help with something, and he will be there for you. He helps family and friends alike by sharing all that he has. There are so many wonderful memories spent on Lake Conroe at their home that they generously shared with everyone. Cousins playing together, sailing, tennis, swimming or just sitting around laughing. I cannot look at a red Solo cup without thinking about him and summertime on Lake Conroe.

My uncle is not a boastful man. He is a very successful business man having run a stainless-steel manufacturing company for many years. It takes a little coaxing and you might get a story or two from him about a project, large or small, that he worked on. Each story having a twist and turn and some funny anecdote.

When I think of my uncle, I always think of a quiet, strong man. A man who smiles when he is entertained by something. There are things or objects that remind me of him. A Chevy Blazer, like the one he drove to New Mexico for our ski trip. A ski boat, especially one with gold trim, like the one I learned to water ski behind. Tennis racquets, from when he and my aunt played doubles tennis.

I have seen first-hand how he cared for my aunt when she was terminally ill. He barely left her side and when he was at her side, he was holding her hand, rubbing her arm and talking to her in a loving voice. He showed me what true love and dedication looks like. He always doted on her and they shared such a wonderful life together. I truly believe they were each other's best friends.

My uncle would do anything to protect his family. He and my aunt were robbed one day on their way back from the grocery store. They were followed home by thieves that robbed them in their driveway. My uncle tried to stop one of the men by throwing his car in reverse in an attempt to hit him and prevent him from getting to my aunt.

He and my cousin made it possible for my aunt to see my new house by surprising me with a visit that I did not know was possible. It took a lot of arranging and coordinating, but they made it happen knowing what it would mean to me. Each time I visited her during the construction phase I kept her updated on the progress and would talk to her about design selections. I cherish the memory of getting to share our new home with her and my uncle.

His home took on four feet of water during Hurricane Harvey because of the unannounced dam release. Their beautiful home that my aunt had decorated from top to bottom, was destroyed. He and my cousins did everything they could to save as much as possible by moving what they could upstairs. He lost so much and through it all he maintained a positive outlook. I cannot begin to put myself in his place and understand the devastation that he experienced. Watching from my viewpoint, he handled everything as he always does, with strength, dignity and grace. If I am ever in a situation where I am being challenged, I have his example to lean on and learn from.

My uncle has not taught me anything because he told me, my uncle has taught me by observing him and learning from his example. An example I am thankful to have in my life and cherish deeply.

Dedicated to Don Harman
Thank you for being a constant in my life
and for all that you've done for me.

Six Lessons and a Crooked Grin

by Harlan Meischen

Lesson #1: A job done right is one you can be proud of. For the third time in as many hours driving circles around the field, I stopped the tractor, jumped down, jogged behind the hay cutter and pulled a strip of missed grass by hand. It was a small strip, only about four inches wide and roughly six feet long. The uncut dark green grass stood out like a beacon against the tan ground and cut grass around it. In the scheme of things, I was cutting a total of 20 acres and that small amount of missed grass was the equivalent of a grain of sand on the beach. Yet, it wasn't done right. It was something my grandfather, JD Rubac, would mention when he came to check on me later in the day. He had a way of pointing things out that wasn't aggressive or punitive but somehow made anyone he was talking with feel a need to own it and correct it. Papaw, as we called him, seemed unceasingly to do things right. I was proud of my job when Papaw drove to the field that afternoon.

Lesson #2: Take care of what you have, and it will serve you well. Papaw's equipment, tools, all his possessions were treated with care and respect. When we finished in the fields all the hay equipment was cleaned and prepped for the next use. Not just hose it off clean. I'm talking crawl underneath, open every cover, dig out grass and dirt by hand, spray it off, hand wash, wipe it down clean. Then, grease and spray with a fine mist of oil or diesel to protect it from rust. To this day I don't know anyone that goes to that length caring for their equipment. I also don't know anyone whose equipment lasts as long and as well as Papaw's did. The same went for his tools and shop. Papaw didn't have a huge quantity of tools or equipment. What he did have worked and everyone knew where to find it. He kept his shop clean and organized. Tools had specific locations. Nothing was left lying on the ground or floor. Nothing was thrown in the back of a truck or in a pile. Because of this, he always seemed to have just what was necessary and it never took longer to get ready to work than it did to actually do the work.

Lesson #3: Hard work and dedication pay off. *"Out of the shade and in the heat. Off your ass and on your feet. Let's go, boy!"* Papaw quoted this phrase often. Work ethic was never a question. There was no sitting around. If there was work to be done, you did it. I rarely remember Papaw taking a break. Even a heart attack and pacemaker didn't slow him down. The doctor said he needed to exercise so he did. Every day without fail he walked faster and further than the rest of the family could match. Hobbies like going fishing were serious business too. Catfish lines were run like clockwork every couple hours to make sure we didn't lose fish. Because of his work ethic, he accomplished more than most during his life. From hitchhiking to Houston and starting a career at the then Diamond Shamrock chemical plant, to retiring as a rancher in the country, Papaw was admired by all that knew him.

Lesson #4: Be thankful for all you have and don't waste. I'll never forget that large chocolate milkshake. My cousin and I were driving between places with Papaw, and we grabbed lunch to go. We were teenage boys at the time with big appetites. We convinced Papaw along with a burger and fries a large milkshake was appropriate. He questioned us once then mentioned that it was fine provided we didn't waste anything. The burger and fries went down quickly. The milkshake, on the other hand, did not. Noticing it was taking a while to finish the shakes, Papaw casually shared his belief in not wasting food. He noted the hard-earned money it cost and all the people in the world going without and how they would beg for just a scrap. I choked down the last of that shake as we turned onto the final stretch of gravel road to the house. My stomach felt miserable. To this day I've never ordered another large milkshake. We are truly blessed to have all that we do, and yet we take so much for granted.

Lesson #5: Giving is about helping others, not about recognition. At Papaw's funeral, the priest shared a story about him I'll never forget. Several years prior, during Sunday mass it was announced to the congregation that the church's private school was struggling financially and facing the reality of closing. After mass Papaw approached the priest to ask how much money the school needed to bridge the gap. The next day Papaw brought a check for that amount with one condition, that he not be recognized. Simply keep the school open. We'd have never known if the priest didn't share that story. To me this was profound. I often wonder who else Papaw helped along the way, silently and humbly. I find myself pausing in awe as I write this paragraph. What would be the impact to our world if we all followed Papaw's lead?

Lesson #6: Dancing is great exercise, a great social activity and to do it well you need to be loose like a dishrag. Dancing was hands down Papaw's favorite pastime. If there was a polka & waltz dance at Sweet Home, Yoakum, Hallettsville, or Mustang Hall you'd likely find Grandma and Papaw in attendance. Light on his feet and full of energy, Papaw was a popular dance partner for all the ladies. It was quite entertaining watching my grandma, mom, or aunt finish a dance with papaw and walk back to the table out of breath, thankful Papaw was headed off to ask another lady to dance the next piece. He would tell us grandkids when dancing we need "be loose like a dishrag". Little did I know his popularity at the dances and his famous dishrag phrase would come into play years later when I asked the girl that is now my wife about her Czech shirt and if she knew how to polka and waltz. She had been at some of those dances and received the same advice from Papaw years before. We now love to go dancing and are complimented often. We laugh and attribute it to being "loose like a dishrag!"

Reflecting on these lessons makes me smile, which brings me to the slightly crooked grin. In every picture of him, every time he pointed out a spot missed in the field, a fitting I forgot to grease, a tool I left out, the food wasted, and every time he rounded the dance floor you could see him grinning, slightly crooked. I suspect it was partly because he knew he was teaching valuable lessons and partly because he was having a great time in the process. I still see that grin every day when I look in the mirror. Yep, he passed that along too!

Papaw, I am eternally grateful for the lessons you taught. They have served me well and in writing this I'm reminded to reflect on them more often. I'm working to pass them to my boys and hopefully my grandchildren… with a slightly crooked grin.

For JD Rubac, and the grandparents in this world you are invaluable and though it may not appear so, we're listening.

It Started with a Cup of Coffee... and I Don't Even Drink Coffee!

by Darlena Eggebrecht

I met my friend Lexy back in September of 2004 when we both worked for a large recruiting firm. I had always been one of those people who liked to go into the office early and be the first person there to get my day lined out and organized with a checklist, so I didn't feel rushed or unorganized. Turns out, Lexy was too. It didn't take long for us to realize we were immediately connected at the soul and a lifetime friendship was on the verge of deliverance.

Since I wasn't a coffee drinker, Lexy taught me how to make a pot of coffee. From that moment on, I had a freshly brewed, hot pot of coffee ready for her when she walked in the door every morning. My time alone to get organized and ready for the day to start was now "our time" together. Lexy had her cup of coffee in hand, and I had my glass of juice. In those 30 – 45 minutes alone

every morning, we built a genuine, trusting, loving, sup-
portive relationship in that office over her cup of coffee.

You see, Lexy and I were both going through some
rough patches in our personal lives during this time, and
we were on a mission to get things right on our journey
in life from this point on. I was going through a divorce,
and she was working through an unhealthy relationship
herself. I had a checklist of things I needed to do in order
to take control of my life again. Divorce – check. New
vehicle – check. Find a job   check. The list went on.

In December, Lexy resigned from the company and
started interviewing with other recruiting firms in the
area. One day she called me up and asked if I wanted to
go to lunch with her and talk about this job interview
that she had just been on. She picked me up from my
office and as we were driving away, she proceeded to tell
me that she saw this ad in the paper for an HR Admin-
istrator. The job was nowhere near where Lexy lived; it
was on my side of town. When I asked her why she went
on that interview if it wasn't near her house, she proudly
said, *"I didn't interview for me, I interviewed for you!"* In
shock, I said, *"What???"* She laughed and said, *"You're
working, and I knew you didn't have the time to interview,
so I did it for you."* Lexy began dialing her cell phone as
she continued to tell me what happened.

She said when the interview started that she told
the girl she wasn't there to interview for herself; she was
there to interview for her friend, Darlena. The girl asked
her, *"Why can't your friend Darlena interview for herself?"*
And Lexy told her, *"Because she doesn't have time to interview, but I do. And she doesn't know she's looking for a job."*
Still in total disbelief, my mouth wide open, a perplexed

look on my face, and eyebrows raised, I looked at Lexy and said, *"And she continued your interview????"* Lexy laughed again and said, *"Yes, and she wants to talk to you."* She handed me the phone.

"Hello," I heard on the line. I said, *"Hello, this is Darlena, Lexy's friend."* The girl on the other end of the line said, *"I understand that I just have to meet you."* I told her, *"That's what I hear too. However, I'm not looking for a job right now."* The girl laughed and said to me, *"Lexy told me you were going to say that..."* I looked over at Lexy, and she was smiling and shaking her head yes. The girl on the phone continued, *"...but she told me that I just have to meet you, and to not take no for an answer. She tells me you are the perfect person for this job."* I tried to apologize again and tell the voice on the other end of the line that I just started a new job 3 months prior and that seriously, I wasn't looking for a job. The conversation went back and forth like that for a couple more times. Finally, we agreed, for Lexy's sake, that I would at least send her my resume when I got back to the office.

I hung up the phone, and Lexy began laughing hysterically, all the while telling me that this was going to be my new job! She said it was perfect for me and it would only be 10 minutes from my home. I said, *"Lexy, you know I have my checklist, and nowhere on that list does it say I need another job. Job is already checked; I'm on to the next thing, and I need to focus."* She said she knew that but that when she read this ad in the paper, something told her it was for me and that she just had to go see.

Do you believe that there is a reason for everything? I do. In this case there was a reason I was supposed to meet Lexy and bond over a cup of coffee. There was a reason Lexy quit her job and saw the ad in the paper to begin with. There was a reason the girl on the other end of the line didn't ask Lexy to leave the moment Lexy said she wasn't interviewing for herself, but for a girl named Darlena. There was even a reason that the job offer that was presented to me was too good to pass up. Yes, it turns out the position was the perfect job for me. Once all was said and done, I accepted the offer with the company and began working for them 3-weeks later. Little did I know, taking that job would change everything for me. Everything!

You see, it's not that I needed a different job, because like I told you, I had a job – check. Why I needed THAT job was because working there would start a domino effect of changing my life and my family's life forever. As it turns out, the husband of the girl that Lexy interviewed with was friends with a man named Joel Eggebrecht, and 6 months after working there, they made an introduction. Two years later, I married that man, and I've never been happier in my life! This story doesn't stop there. My husband was friends with a family for years that had a little girl he had known since she was 3-years-old. When she was 16, she came to Joel's 50th birthday party and that is where my youngest son met her for the first time. 10 years later, that little girl is now our daughter-in-law. Then there is the fact that my grandchildren have a Pa-J. Trust me when I say, my entire family is grateful for Joel for various reasons; however, he's icing on the cake as a grandfather. All of this, and MORE, much, much more, because Lexy went on that interview, for me!

I never knew that by learning to make a pot of coffee for a friend would change my life forever, but it did!

Oh, and for those of you who think how gutsy it was for Lexy to interview for me... well, she did it to me again, nearly 3 years later, but I'll leave that story for another day.

> For Lexy Thompson, the one who created the
> foundation that would change my life forever.
> I will always have a cup of coffee waiting for you!

Little White Lie

by Jennifer Victoria Bell

My father and I did not have the best of relationships. He was controlling, and at times, very distant. If he was angry with you, you could expect the silent treatment for a while.

He also loved to make me laugh, loved to surprise me, and, at times, he let me know he completely understood me.

When I was 17, he bought me a car. It was a 1979 AMC Jeep Truck (my favorite vehicle still to this day) and it was a 3-speed manual transmission. I did not know how to drive manual, I learned on an automatic.

I went thru some painstaking driving lessons with my mother. No matter what she said, I could not figure out how to drive that truck.

After one of those times, where I just wanted to growl at my mother in frustration, we met my father for dinner at the Apollo Diner on route 33 in Farmingdale, NJ.

My mother and I came in and he knew it was not a good drive. We told him that we have a communication issue and laughed because she couldn't teach me to canoe either.

He took out his blue felt tip pen from his shirt pocket and began to draw a manual transmission engine and described what happens when you step on the clutch and switch gears.

It was like a miracle. I felt my brain relax and expand and all the growling frustration melted away. I got in my truck, named Timmy by the way, and drove it like I had been driving stick for years.

My father knew. He saw me and knew exactly what I needed. He knew in that moment how my mind worked, and I felt really seen for the first time in my life. It is one of my most favorite memories of him.

He passed in 2007 and gave me the greatest gift.

We weren't talking to each other when he was diagnosed with malignant melanoma. He married a woman who was extremely jealous of any attention my father gave to another woman, even his own daughter. That jealousy caused so much conflict that my father basically stopped talking to me. It was the longest silent treatment I had ever experienced with him, and it hurt. I broke the silent spell and called him to let him know I was thinking of him, that I loved him and that I could help him since at that time I was a licensed acupuncturist. He was still a bit icy, but that conversation began the thaw.

He decided to try acupuncture but, wanted a referral for an expert. Satiating that controlling nature, I referred him to a colleague. He called me after the first treatment and exclaimed, *"I believe in the power of acupuncture!"* He was genuinely overjoyed and elated about how his body felt after his first treatment. It warmed my heart that I could support him, and we got close again. We spoke on the phone almost every day as my dad drove home from his job in NYC.

What was interesting is that the melanoma did not spread internally in my father's body. It just kept producing tumors that were being pushed out of his skin. He had surgery after surgery to remove them and had chemo as well. To look at my Dad, you would never know he was undergoing any kind of treatment. He always had a big belly, a robust ruddy complexion and sparkling blue eyes, which by the way, I was the only child to inherit those. His robust appearance shifted after a round with a new chemo med.

I went to his house and his face shape and color changed. He went from round to long and drawn and from robust and ruddy to ashen gray. I knew the chemo was weakening his system and not supporting it at this point. He finally let go of control and allowed me to help him with acupuncture and acupressure a few months before, so I wasn't surprised when he asked me to help him die.

On Sunday, July 22, 2007, my father had a heart attack and fell backward in the tub and cracked his head open a bit. I got the call to go to the hospital where I was born, that was where they were taking him and I felt that it would be okay, hearing which hospital he was going to. But then, the phone rang again, and I was told he was being taken to the hospital that he was born in. At that moment, I knew he was going to die.

I rushed to the hospital and met him in the emergency room with my sister and his wife. His red color was back but I knew it was because of the trauma. I did everything I could with acupressure and energy healing to help calm him and keep him relaxed. When we had a moment alone, he said, *"Jenn, you have to help me die."* He didn't really ask me, he told me. He said he was extremely uncomfortable, and he was ready to go. So, he asked me the way he asked for everything, he told me that I had to. And I said I would.

Here is how I helped him die. I lied to him. The doctors told us that the cancer had spread to his stomach and brain, and that he had just one lung lobe that was cancer free. This is a testament to the strength of his body, driving into NYC every day for 10-hour work days with no apparent sign of distress. I know he would want people to know about how strong he was. To give you an idea of just how strong, he could bring a grown man to their knees just by squeezing their hand.

Now back to the lie. When they moved him into his own room in the hospital, we had a moment alone again. He asked me what was going on. I told him how far his cancer had spread and added this lie. I said that the doctors didn't think he would make it through the night. And he said, *"That would be good."* The doctors never said that. But I knew my controlling father would not let go of his body unless someone in a position of authority told him it was time.

I spent the night alone with my Dad, watching him breathe, utter words in his morphined state. I told him that he was the best Dad a little girl could have and that I loved him. He passed the next morning.

The gift I am so thankful for is this: Words carry weight. Words create. Every word is an opportunity to offer love. In this case, 11 words helped my father to feel safe enough to die.

This is dedicated to the best Dad a little girl could ever have. Thank you Robert William Belikoff for shaping my life with your love. Here is the only picture I have of the 2 of us from when I was a little girl.

Jennifer Victoria Bell, Teacher of Metaphysical Teachers & the Founder of the Devotion School of Sovereign Soul Technologies. www.jennifervictoriabell.com/

An Adoption Adventure

by Melanie Rose

"Anyone who ever wondered how much they could love a child who did not spring from their own loins, know this: it is the same. The feeling of love is so profound, it's incredible and surprising."

— **Nia Vardalos, Instant Mom**

Little did the Fed Ex guy know as he pulled in front of my house that he was about to be ambushed. I armed myself as he walked up the driveway. Though it seemed an eternity, only seconds passed as he made it to the door. I was ready and waiting. He never had a chance to ring the doorbell. I flung open the door and aimed directly at him. The Fed Ex guy was taken aback. Startled he asked, *"What's going on?!"*

I exclaimed, *"That's my brown envelope! I have to take your picture!"*

"What for?" he questioned nervously as he backed up.

"That's my baby in there!" I said excitedly, pointing to the envelope. *"I'm adopting a baby girl from China! That's her picture and all of her information! You're delivering her! You're my stork!"*

"Really? Cool!" He smiled broadly, held up the envelope and I snapped away.

The next three weeks passed in a flurry of activity and excitement. 'What to pack? What to wear? What gifts should I purchase for the officials? What does a one-year-old need?' These were just some of the questions running through my head as I prepared to embark on the most important journey of my life.

I left for China on September 1st. Crossing the International Dateline, our plane arrived in Guangzhou on the 3rd. How odd it seemed to lose an entire day of my life knowing that I would never get it back. My journal would be forever blank on September 2, 2002.

At the airport, our translator, Henry, met me and the others who would make up our small travel group – five families in all. I was the only person in our group not traveling with a spouse or friend to help me. Henry had a van waiting to take us to the White Swan Hotel on Shamian Island, which would become home for the next two weeks.

Upon arrival at the hotel, Henry called a brief meeting to say that we would be leaving in one hour to receive our babies. After Henry explained what paperwork, fees, and gifts we needed to bring, we rushed to our rooms to freshen up, gather our important documents, gifts, orphanage donations, cameras, and pack our diaper bags.

Even though I was exhausted from having essentially no sleep in two days, I scurried to gather my belongings and quickly rushed back down to the lobby. Virtually 'pregnant' for 23 months (the gestation period of an elephant is only 22!), which was the time it took to do the paperwork and wait for my referral, I could not believe that I was about to hold my daughter in my arms for the first time!

Driving to the CCAA (China Center for Adoption Affairs) allowed us the opportunity to see some of the diversity in China for the first time. The driving habits of the Chinese (our driver included) from the airport to the hotel had already made us fearful of venturing out by auto. It was a toss-up as to who had the right of way – the vehicles, the pedestrians who would step off a sidewalk seemingly uninterested in whether or not a vehicle was going to stop for them, or the bicycles with baskets and wares piled at least three times as high as its driver. Leaving a very Westernized city and our 5-star hotel, our drive led us through farm areas, rice paddies with people working in the fields, and a water buffalo lying on the side of the road watching the cars and people pass by.

Finally, we reached the CCAA. We were given very brief instructions of what would happen and advised that they were about to introduce the babies. Within minutes, the first baby was introduced. Not mine. The second baby was brought out. Before her name was called, I recognized her immediately. It was my Tia looking even more beautiful than the photo that had been sent to me. I fell instantly in love, but Tia had other ideas. As

I reached to take her in my arms, she opened her mouth and screamed! I am sure she was thinking, 'Who is this strange white woman and what is she going to do with me?!'

The other four babies were calm, curious, and looking around at everyone. Tia continued to scream and cry incessantly! She cried the entire time we were at the CCAA to complete our paperwork. I took slight solace in that other people tried to hold her, and she screamed just as loud with them. One gentleman in our group asked if he could lay hands and pray over her. I was willing to try anything. He laid hands, we both prayed, and she still screamed.

It wasn't until we arrived back at our hotel a few hours later that she finally stopped. I was unsure if she was tired from all of the screaming, or simply just interested in her new surroundings. She toddled around looking at every inch of the hotel room. Her favorite thing was for me to pick her up and let her see herself in the large mirror. For all I know it was the first time she had seen her reflection. She was fascinated.

The next day Tia and I headed downstairs to the breakfast buffet to dine with our group. According to the paperwork I received, at 15-months Tia's diet still consisted of formula and rice cereal with occasional mashed fruit. As we stood in front of the massive amount of food, Tia's little eyes grew the size of saucers.

I put a few things on her plate such as scrambled eggs, grapes, and rice not knowing what she would like. She scarfed everything down. Next, she had some yogurt. That went down quickly. I got her some noodles, bacon, and orange slices. With only eight front teeth and having to gnaw the food, she ate everything I put in front of her. I literally had to stop her from eating, afraid she would make herself sick. She may have only started with eight teeth when I received her, but before we left China, she had a mouth full. The combination of good, nutritious food and working her gums caused all of her teeth to come in at once! No teething problems!

On Wednesday, Henry advised that he arranged for us to visit the orphanage where our daughters had been living. The babies seemed to enjoy riding in the van. All was well until we pulled into the driveway of the orphanage. Tia apparently recognized where we were and the screaming began again. She cried when the orphanage director held her. She cried when her former nannies held her. The crying only stopped when we climbed back in the van, pulled out of the drive, and headed back to the hotel. Tia snuggled into me and fell asleep. I was heartbroken as I realized Tia must have thought I was taking her back to the orphanage and she did not want to go.

Even though I would be in China for 10 more days to complete the adoption process, I was at peace. In that instant of her snuggling down and falling asleep, I knew that she was forever and truly mine. My baby girl had bonded with me.

Dedicated to my daughter who makes me proud
every single day. You are my greatest love and
best friend. I can't imagine my life without you,
and I can't wait to see where your journey
in life leads. I'll love you forever, Mom.

In My Mother's House

by Sara Lovell

I cannot see a butterfly without thinking of my mom. I remember as a child playing in the garage in my mother's house and finding her old hard hat that had butterfly stickers all over it. I asked why she did that. She said that when she worked construction, she was the only woman in her crew and the guys would always steal her hardhats. So, she put butterfly stickers on it so that wouldn't happen anymore. I played with that for years. I also remember her telling me that when I was little and I saw her butterfly tattoo on her stomach I would say,

"Mommy, you have a bug on your belly"

I am so much like her and the older I get the more I realize and appreciate this. My friends tell me whenever I strike up a conversation with a complete stranger,

"That's our Sara, making friends wherever she goes" I giggle and think, I must get that from my om. I know how important it is to surround myself with good and fun people! She taught me how to make and be a good friend to many. These life-long friends of hers became important mentors to me and were a constant in my mother's house.

When I think of Mom and my childhood, music and dancing are usually part of my memories. She would teach me line dances, the bump, and many dances to all types of music. My dynamic and broad love of music and dance I owe to her. I smile when I think of fun memories of dear family and friends dancing in her living room at every party in my mother's house.

I am so grateful for her bravery in creating a special family with her partner of now of 38 years, Helene. Together, the two of them provided us with a loving home. They taught us what a loving family feels like, even if it wasn't quite the same as what other families looked like in the 80s and 90s. My mom taught me how to pray and how to have a personal relationship with God and a respect for spirituality. She would drive for three days straight with kids and dogs in tow every single summer vacation to make sure that we knew and developed relationships with our family in Utah, where she grew up in her mother's house.

My mom was always there for everything that I needed, whether it was practicing for my spelling tests, sitting in my classroom all day when I was misbehaving in elementary school, being my girl scout leader, my homeroom parent, attending softball games, carpooling for violin practice, countless dance practices and recitals, showing me what it means to honor our commitments, taking us to church and showing us how important it was to be a part of a fellowship, being a mom with the moms-and-pops-of-props for the drill team, going back to work to help pay for braces and dance, giving me my first job of assisting her with wallpapering and painting, then encouraging me to get an education, not letting me date until I was 16 years old, busting my butt for not coming home on time… the list goes on and on.

Perhaps one of the most crucial times she was there for me was when I was 17 and sick. She listened to her gut and questioned the doctor and rushed me to the hospital to discover in the emergency room that I had a nearly fatal type of meningitis. She stayed by my side in the hospital for a week. Then at home, she learned how to give me the necessary IV treatments and wouldn't let anyone else do it. When I was recovering, she sweet-talked the local gym into letting me have a membership even though I wasn't old enough yet so I could build my endurance up again.

I moved out of my mother's house to attend college in Utah. I will never EVER forget the look on her face when she drove away from my tiny apartment in Provo to go back to her house in Texas. With tears in both our eyes, it was a look of loving me enough to let me go. A look that said it was time for me to experience being a young adult for myself even though I could see, I would always be her baby girl.

The final time I left my mother's house was the day after she threw my 21st birthday party. She stood by my side while many in my life didn't understand my decision to leave Texas again this time, to work in Alaska for the summer. When I fell in love and decided to move to Alaska permanently, I came back to get my car and whatever I could fit in it. Then she drove over 2,000 miles with me and made sure I was settled in the last frontier, on my own, without her again.

Soon, I decided to get married and she helped me organize and plan my wedding from a distance and made sure that it was the perfect day for me and my groom. We bought a home of our own and any time I had a question about my house or how to fix anything, she was just a phone call away. She was my expert in creating a loving home. And when my marriage fell apart six years later, my mom got on the first flight to be there with me as I felt so broken and alone with a one-year-old baby. We worked together on my house and my yard to create a safe and beautiful place for me and my son to make a new normal. To make our house a home, just like hers had been for me.

A few years ago I was listening to Corinne Bailey Rae's album. I remembered listening to her music in my mother's house. I heard a song called, *Butterfly* and as I listened to the words I wept with grateful emotion for the love I have for my mom. The first lyric is,

> *"In my Mother's house, there's a photograph, of a day gone past, always makes me laugh..."*

It reminded me so much of her and of the two of us. As her daughter, I am so grateful for my mom and for all the things that she has done for me.

For my mom, Dorothy May Lovell, my best friend.
To the dazzling woman who taught me how
to live, laugh, love and be myself. You give
me love, like a butterfly...
I love you!

A Heart That Overflows

by Elise Adam Buck

Throughout the course of this lifetime, the love you have for a parent definitely evolves as you grow in your own personal journey through life. It is this beautiful journey that feels so wonderful when I think of the love that I have for my father. As a child, I can remember him bouncing me on his knee singing the "giddy up," song all the while I was laughing uncontrollably. The fun, the love, the overall sense of being the most special person on earth was everything that my father exuberated. His strong sense of work ethic made me want to work harder at anything I set out to accomplish. His big, kind heart made me want to embrace everyone with just a little more attention, a little more comfort, and with an added sense of gratitude. While you are going through this journey, you have no idea how it is literally shaping you: who you are, how you feel about things, how you react to things, to people. What a precious gift this truly is to feel the heartbeat of a great big man whose **Heart Overflows**.

Upon landing my first job at the Thom McAn Shoe Store, I explained to my father that I received an hourly rate of pay *plus commission*. He asked me to explain the "commission." I outlined to him that it was based on sales volume in addition to point of purchase sales... selling things like shoelaces, shoe polish, canvas/leather conditioners, etc. My father carefully outlined how I could increase my sales on these point of purchase items by "simply being me," he said. Through the gift of gab, I empowered people to really see how they needed the shoe polish (it would extend the life of the shoe after all), or how they really should always have an "extra" pair of shoe laces. Every payday and I truly mean EVERY payday, my father would ask me how I did on my commissions. He'd encourage me to keep up the good work. Before long, I realized that my commissions were exceeding my hourly rate of pay. It was through this constant encouragement and praising process that I truly gained insight into becoming a better salesman. Again, this *Heart That Overflows* was making me a better person.

Throughout my years in high school and along the journey of life, the picture of this influence became crystal clear in regard to my father's selflessness. The beauty of its evolution was that he had no idea he was doing it, but he was most definitely helping me become a better person. He continued to do this through encouragement, through love, and through setting a great example. Coming from a strong sense of family heritage, my father never failed to raise us without a constant reminder of how important the family is to our wellbeing. My father himself was raised by parents who taught the value of loyalty to the community and your fellow man. Day in and day out, the family was our nucleus to all things – our first cousins were our playmates, our aunts and uncles were just blocks away, and our grandfather and grandmother lived at the end of the lane. This shaped us most definitely. Again, the *Heart That Overflows* was making me a better person.

What a sense of gratitude I have toward this most awesome man. He is a true best friend who always has my best interest in mind. He is a beautiful and caring spirit. I have such a distinct memory of the day that I moved into my dorm room my freshman year at college. There I stood telling the man who had shaped me into who I was "Good Bye." It truly was a life altering event! While I was excited and felt like I was on top of the world... How was I going to let go? This was it. It was time, and I never looked back. Although different, the encouragement was the same, the support was still there, and very few days went by without a phone call to catch up. Still, the *Heart That Overflows* was making me a better person.

Moving through life and finding out who you are, where you came from, and where you wish to be is truly an experience. Your sense of self is challenged, and you begin to have your own set of core values. You stumble, you learn, and it all goes into a little memory bank of sorts that shapes who you are and what kind of person you have become. My father is never far from my thoughts in anything that I set out to accomplish. I have come to realize that this is part of my inner strength and a part of me that he helped create through his constant encouragement. What a gift. It has since become an even bigger gift in that my own children now benefit from these most precious traits that my father has given this world. As teenagers, my own children are so extremely close with my father and they, too, are benefitting from all that he has to offer. Again, the *Heart That Overflows* continues to make me a better person and now is making my children better people.

When I was a very young age, my father and his twin brother began to purchase property in the central region of the state in which we live. This property quickly became a place for us to enjoy weekends, enjoy holidays, and enjoy very precious time with family. For over 50 years now, this property has been an outlet for us to experience so many beautiful times together as a family. We have created memories for a lifetime and we have had endless days enjoying our family at this most precious spot. It was my Dad's vision, along with his twin brother in regard to this property that has given us so much joy. It is with great gratitude that I reflect back on the vision he had with his brother and see it as such a value added for my upbringing and that of my own children. Thank you, Dad, – I love who you are, I love what you stand for, and I love your heart. It is most definitely a *Heart That Overflows.*

Dedicated to Jerry J. Adam, Sr.
For my father who has always had a
Heart That Overflows.

The Art of Receiving

by Valerie Bottazzi

Being an outcast for most of my life hurt me deeply building into my unworthiness. Ever since I was a little girl I never felt that I belonged in any community, tribe, school or club. I have always been the odd one out. A painful memory from the day of my 5th nephew's baptism drilled this feeling even further. During that celebratory morning, right after the ceremony, outside the church and throughout the whole day at home, the family took pictures of the group. First the adults, then the teenagers, then the babies… yet I wasn't allowed in any group picture because I wasn't an adult, neither a teenager nor a toddler. I was 9, the only one in no-man's-land. My mother found me later on crying in the garden and tried her best to fix the situation, by making a show of having me at the center of a picture with my 5 nieces and nephews. The picture is quite nice, yet still, today, when I see it, I am reminded of the pain of not knowing where I belonged… until I met him.

Born and raised in Argentina, daughter of two Italians, I left Buenos Aires at the age of 27. Buying into the spell that immigrants have to fend for themselves, as I moved from one international location to another, I lived with the concept that I alone had to carry the weight of the world on my shoulders. It was never mirrored that it is all right to receive help, that it is okay to let others protect me; I never felt I could belong to any group, and of course, life confirmed this belief many times over!

When I first saw Stefano I had been through one of the roughest times in my life. I had just separated from the father of my children. As I kept raising the professional bar for myself, being the sole breadwinner for the family and becoming more powerful and capable in the corporate world, I was sliding down the path of a "woe is me/pitiful/victimhood /I am unworthy" illusion. What a dark night of the soul those years were!

I started biking as a way to heal from the pain of the divorce. Riding my bicycle through the rolling hills in Tuscany became a necessity, and as my body pumped endorphins into my system, I started to feel alive and healthy once again. It was precisely during my first amateur bike ride that I met the man that was to become my third husband. My soul recognized him before my ego did, however, it took two years of joking and flirting at bike gatherings before we started dating.

Stefano and I could not have had two more dissimilar backgrounds. Picture this: his birth town, a medieval town near Siena, has a population of 2,000 people, whereas mine has 26 million! While I moved and traveled around the world he had stayed at home. While in the corporate world I was responsible for southern Europe and the Middle East, he owned a family business where he worked side by side with his parents and his younger brother as wood artisans.

When Stefano decided to start dating me, he felt he was taking a big risk- understandably so, since at the time he was single and in his 40's - joining a "crazy international divorcee with two children"! We both embraced the challenge of living life as the best version of ourselves, and most importantly, he taught me what it means to have someone playing on your team, supporting you and accepting your desires unconditionally. Stefano made me feel I "belonged"... to our team, the team of one another and the team of 4 that included my two amazing sons.

Our first 9 years together felt like running an obstacle race as life kept throwing all kinds of wrenches into our paths! We had financial breakdowns and breakthroughs, lawsuits, family discord, and health issues.

Health issues are a key part of this story, as my body broke down creating a "dual hip osteoarthritis" commonly known as degenerative joint disease. In the span of 4 years, I went from being a strong, fit, healthy, sportive woman in her forties, to being a literally crippled with excruciating pain 24/7 woman in her fifties! It went downhill from there to include my inability to lift my legs, stand freely, put on my socks or pants, not to mention walk or tie my shoes!

This blessing in disguise was the final straw that cracked me fully open. Me, the one with a lifetime fending for myself, of doing it all, of being the sole breadwinner, of cooking-cleaning-grocery-shopping and oh, by the way, meanwhile being a successful entrepreneur, single mom, daughter, sister, friend, and lover...did I forget something?

My whole infrastructure crumbled like a house of cards. Nothing could hold it up anymore, nor could I hold myself up either! I felt shame from being sick and was forced to confront the monsters inside my head telling me all kinds of mean things. When asking for help I felt guilty and victimized. I didn't know how to ask for help, and most importantly, I didn't know how to receive it.

Stefano's generous heart and incredibly patient personality showed me his joy in being of loving service. I cannot count the times when he repeated, *"Val, you are no longer alone, you have me, and you have your sons"*. But it wasn't his words that did it but rather his congruency. His actions spoke so loud, his loving acts of service showed me so clearly that I could relinquish fear and lean into the unknown that it made me feel safe; safe enough to learn the art of receiving. He took over all the tasks I could no longer do on my own any more. He was my caregiver.

With his ability to give so freely, so generously and so lovingly, Stefano helped me connect the dots... He is and has been my teacher of the art of receiving. As an imbalanced giver, I had always felt that in order to receive just a little I had to give tenfold beforehand. I hadn't understood how critical the breath of giving and receiving is in order to enjoy healthy relationships, until now.

My bighearted man taught me the power of belonging to a tribe, through his powerful, humble, great love he supported me as I let go of my fears and I opened up to receive all that was being given. His ability to give without holding anything back, while being so clear in the joy he felt while giving, helped me understand the gift inherent in receiving. Learning to receive is and has been a key gateway to live my life on purpose as a life coach and healer while living a fulfilling joy-filled life as an empowered woman.

Dedicated to Stefano Ricci
I am most grateful to all who had a role in my body and soul's healing path, and especially Stefano Ricci, who has been a balm to my scars... to you I dedicate this story.

Valerie Bottazzi, Love Coach & Healer
www.ValerieBottazzi.com
Valerie@ValerieBottazzi.com

The Man Who Loved Me

by Tarah Sutton

I died. On 11/11/11, I died. This man saved my life.

I grew up in the suburbs, white picket fence, middle daughter, married parents, normal, basic, all American life. Although my upbringing was the 'norm' and I cannot say we lacked for anything, I always felt bored, and rather empty. I was always looking for something more. So, like most young people I turned to my friends for understanding and to find what I was looking for, to find myself.

From the age of sixteen throughout my twenties, I partied a lot, created a lot of drama and eventually found myself depressed and drinking wine fairly often. It was fine. I was fine. That's everyone, right?

Little did I know, there was someone watching me. Unbeknownst to me, he had known me my whole life. He was always following me and checking on me. I didn't even know he was there. He was watching me when I was doing unthinkable things. He was listening when I was saying things that could only break hearts.

He was always there. Just watching and waiting.

At the time I met him, I was living in Colorado with my Husband and my first-born son. I remember the first time I saw him. My friend invited me to this local church, and I was completely uninterested and gave excuse after excuse as to why I couldn't make it. I feel bad about that now. I should have gone. Eventually, I couldn't say no anymore, so I begrudgingly went with her.

I remember walking into church that day, I remember the smell of the foyer and the smell of the perfume of the lady that greeted me at the door. It was so strangely wonderful. I walked into the sanctuary and the worship music began to play. Not like the hymns when I was growing up, but it was music that was made just for me. The pastor was there, arms raised to the heavens, eyes closed. I looked around, everyone was immersed in the music. It was so beautiful.

I remember closing my eyes to listen to the music, and there He was. He was standing down in the front of the room with his arms wide open to me. He was staring right at me, everyone in the room disappeared. Everything went silent. I couldn't breathe. I had never felt anything like this before and I couldn't comprehend the overwhelming sense of love.

I began to weep.

For the next year, I attended church regularly. I wanted to see him every day. Everything I was hearing and seeing was remarkable. These people were not like the people I had known in the past. They were different. They all knew Him, and we all worked as if in unison to learn about Him and to help each other understand what He wanted for us.

I didn't know He had a plan for me that was bigger than me. He had created this entire world of blessing and opportunity for me and all I had to do was meet Him.

I am grateful for this man. This man I had not known. He waited so patiently for me to come and see Him. He loved me, throughout my entire life, when I didn't even care to see Him. He was there all along, waiting for me. This man died for me. This man came to this earth and lived just so He could die to save me. To wash me clean of all of my unrighteousness. He died. First, He was publicly humiliated and beaten with a whip that tore His flesh when it landed on Him. Every lashing, He took for me. When He was physically nailed by his hands and feet on the cross, He saw my face. When He was crying out to His Father, He was thinking of me. When He took his last breath, He did it so that I could live.

I died on 11/11/11.

Therefore, if anyone is in Christ he is a new creation; old things have passed away; behold, all things have become new. (2 Corinthians 5:17)

When I was saved, everything changed. It was the weekend the church was having a women's conference and I remember coming home that Saturday and looking my husband in the eye and telling him I had changed and that I was never going to be the same again. I told him that I understood if he couldn't go on the journey with me, but I had to chase Jesus with all of my being.

I am grateful for Jesus. He taught me how to love. He taught me that forgiveness is the only way to be free. He taught me that our time here on earth is limited and that it is my purpose and my right to reach as many people as possible and teach them about Him. Gratitude is more than a feeling. Gratitude is the readiness to show appreciation for and to return the kindness. Gratitude is an action. It is taking what was given to you and showing it to the next person.

I don't know much, but I do know that if you do not know Jesus, He knows you. If you are still looking for your purpose and meaning behind life, He has the answer for you. I would hate for you to go another day without knowing what He has for you. There are people on this earth that need you to meet Him so that they can meet Him. If you do know Him, use this as a reminder that He created you on purpose and that He has so many things He wants to unlock inside of you. Whatever you do, never give up on Him. Press on toward the future. He has beauty and blessings in store for you.

Dedicated to the man I love, Jesus Christ.
I want to dedicate my entire future to Jesus.
Without Him, I am nothing. With Him,
I can do everything.

Enough

by Lisa Schillaci

I remember the setup of the meeting and where everyone was sitting; Dawn and I sat directly across from our Executive CFO, and three Senior Vice Presidents sat to our right. Dawn and I were on opposing sides of an issue, and we had to go to C-Suite to break the tie and determine a mutual path forward. I remember being called to the meeting to defend a computer system that was important to both Dawn's and my departments; and I remember when the meeting ended, I did not feel right. The feeling was heavy and ugly. Moreover, the actions and words I displayed during the meeting were so out of my character. What did I just do? In my defense of the computer system, I valued saving the computer system over the value of our relationship. I had been careless with my words and I was careless with her.

I knew I needed to talk to her; I was consumed with ridding myself of this heaviness. I called her that evening; she did not answer. I texted her later in the evening; she said she "needed some time." Her responses reinforced in my mind that I had blown it. Not only did I blow it with her, but I demeaned her in front of her boss. Another relationship in peril. The heaviness just got heavier.

The date was November 9, 2017.

She needed space; she needed time to gather her thoughts. She needed time to ready herself before she could talk. Waiting for her was agony to me. All I could think about was what I had done to her; how she must have felt; and how much she must hate me.

How could I have been so careless with her? What must she think of me? Will she ever trust me again? It was a blessing that several days passed before we talked. During these days waiting, I was able to evaluate our relationship, how I felt about her, and what I envisioned our future to be.

The first time we talked, it was on the phone. I just listened. And, I apologized. She was gracious to accept my apology. To me, my apology did not seem enough. She then went on Thanksgiving holiday, and I emailed her another apology. In the email, I shared some of my thoughts and was more effusive than our first conversation on the phone. Again, she accepted my apology and told me she had moved on and was able to put it behind her. She is so gracious I thought; still, it did not seem enough. I then asked to speak with her and her boss in person. She said that was not necessary; to me it was everything.

The date for the in-person meeting was November 29, 2017. Twenty days had passed since the incident. I drove 25 miles to meet with her and her boss for a 15-minute face to face meeting. I would have driven 100 miles.

It was just the three of us at a small round table. This meeting meant everything to me. Both Dawn and her boss were gracious, and they both accepted my apology. I left the meeting and drove back 25 miles. In my Gratitude Journal for that day, my notes included words such as "restoration," "her relationship is too important," "think outside of myself," and "second chances."

Dawn accepted my apology the first time; the time I talked to her on the phone. She never gave me a reason to doubt her sincere forgiveness. I'm grateful to Dawn that she modeled the grace of giving forgiveness and allowing me to forgive myself. To me, her forgiveness was more. It was more than the act of forgiving. For 20 days, I challenged myself and wondered if the tables had been turned, did I have it in me to really and truly forgive. This was big for me, and Dawn modeled that for me.

I saw the beauty and magnificence of selflessly and truly forgiving someone and making me feel that I was enough.

The date is now March 5, 2019, and Dawn is one of my besties. She has made it into my Gratitude Journal a couple more times over the past 15 months. We went on a women's retreat together back in October 2018. Our relationship continues to grow and deepen. We both trust each other and have shared personal stories; we have come to rely on each other. For me, it feels light and free to be around her, knowing that she accepts me for me; that I am enough. I am protective of not only our friendship and relationship but also my relationships with others. I've been changed for good. Dawn, thank you!

Enough

Dedicated to Dawn Preston, and to all
who have lost someone; it is never too late to find
them again. Don't let all the thousands of reasons
stop you from attempting restoration and
reconciliation. You are enough.

Crossing the Line

by Linda Glass

Words are meaningful. So, I've learned.
My father suggested that I take Latin since I
was taking so many languages in college. Knowing the
origins of language would be powerful. While I haven't
retained it, it's always made me curious about a word's
beginning. So, let's start there.

gratitude (n.) mid-15c., Latin origin, gratus – pleasing,
thankful

Pleasing… As a child there were things that were
endlessly pleasing to me. Days without schedules creating
make believe lands with my sister. My mom's pies.
Snow days.

There's a point in growing up when you unconsciously
cross the line from happy-go-lucky child (if you're lucky)
to angst. Hormones, social life, the world's weight on
your teenage shoulders. When you cross that line, the
"pleasing" portion becomes a bit more hedonistic and less
innocent. At least it was for me. I was cynical. Judgmental. Pleased by the musings of The Cure and Depeche
Mode.

And in terms of *thankful*? It showed up once in a while when I was given a pass for a late paper or sneaking out to meet my friends. Being thankful wasn't very deep. It certainly wasn't a conscious exercise.

As I'm crossing the line into my 50s, what is pleasing and that for which I'm thankful has shifted greatly. The vision board filled with 80s sensibility of consumption to my vision board of today is very different. It's no longer about what I have or the status I've gained. The board is filled with color – vibrancy – images that represent micro-moments of connection, taking risks and experiencing emotions that remind me I'm alive.

These are moments when my husband cheers me on - showing the ultimate confidence in my ability to take on something new. It happens when I open my son's door in the morning to find him asleep in his bed after a night of not knowing where he is and wondering if he'll be okay. It happens when my sister just sits with me, not talking, but *being there* – giving me space to simply be.

I find myself pausing, eyes closing, saying "thank you" in my head after each moment. I know the BIG moments come and go. I cherish these small expressions of love.

In the spring of 2017, my father was moved into an assisted living facility for memory care. It was time. He didn't want to go nor did he think he needed to live there. But he went out of responsibility, believing it was what my sister needed to be able to care for her husband. For that we were definitely thankful.

I knew the moments I sat with him would be few and far between. And his ability to share details of his life events or musings was waning. I just didn't know how long. I ate up the moments as much as I could. I took in one more recital of the serenity prayer *"Have you heard this? It's so important."* Hearing one more curmudgeon comment, *"Jesus Christ! These people are old."*

Sitting beside him in early June this turned out to be our last true visit together. We sat relaxing after his nap, FOX news muted, my father drinking coffee and me reading. He looked up at me and said a few things. I looked up and nodded. We got back to the relaxing at hand.

Then he spoke.

Great things come to those who cross the line.

I'm sorry, what Dad?

There's a slot. I'm being battered around correctly to get to the slot.

Hmm. Okay... Dad, would you like to stay here and drink your coffee?

I'm watching the news.

Okay... Well, Steve's aunt came to visit us recently from Corpus.

His what?!

His aunt - a - u - n - t.

Huh. a - u - n - t. I don't know what that is.

You know some people don't want to cross the line. They want to play it safe. They want you to stay on

this side of the line and behave, follow all the rules.

That's no way to live. You have to cross the line. You have to live. You live by crossing the line.

And like that, our chat was over. The day went on and I sat staring at him. Wondering how he was feeling. Whether he was sharing that the end was near.

It seemed appropriate that those would be his last words of wisdom to share. He died on July 23, 2017.

My father started crossing the line at an early age. That is when I am certain the shaming started- when he was acting out, unconsciously crossing the line, not following all the rules as expected. His father shamed him. His mother prayed in fear to God. Why can't he just be his brother?

Crossing the line meant living in a way that made sense to him. It was natural. As a child born in 1929, it's not like there was a web forum for his parents to join on how to raise a young boy with Mensa IQ and ADD. He "didn't listen." He "misbehaved." He was pushing the boundaries, both intellectually and physically.

My father never shared that with me directly. However, he wrote a lot. And through the years I picked up bits and pieces of how his childhood went and how he was often scorned for crossing the line. How he used alcohol to feel better. He was brilliant. He was audacious. He was silly. He was clever.

He could also be a know-it-all. Condescending. Belittling. I constantly had to urge myself to practice compassion for the little boy whose self-esteem was threatened.

The thing is, my father spent his life crossing the line, first unconsciously as we all do and then very consciously. When I was younger, I used to feel sorry for him each time he crossed the line and "failed." It never appeared to work out in his favor. At least from my vantage point. Whether he was going to win the judicial election, actually find silver when mining in New Mexico, or getting that huge book deal, he didn't cross the line as a "winner."

I grew to see him as a dreamer with no landing pad. False hopes and no ability to execute. It made me sad.

With my skewed perception I judged him. A lot. In turn, my adulthood focused on landing things, since he didn't and feeling utter shame when I left my work, my art, my projects, incomplete.

Would my father's life had been richer if he had accomplished all those things? He would say no. Emphatically.

Was he telling me to stop judging by outcomes? I think so.

He spent his sober adulthood getting out of judgement and focusing on gratitude. Gratitude for crossing the line. And in his later years, more and more gratitude for the micro moments with the Indiana trees, his family, and the beautiful taste of apple pie.

A pleasing life filled with gratitude is one where you knowingly cross the line and enjoy every little step along the way. Thanks, Dad. For these lessons, I am truly grateful.

Dedicated to my dad, one handsome son of a bitch (*self-proclaimed*) who loved grammar, Indiana and his family. Oh, and a good sense of humor. Miss you.

George Glass and
Linda Glass circa 1978

Carrie

by Lynette Adam

There have been many who have impacted my life through the years. But as I think of these, one comes to my mind over and over…my maternal grandmother. She was an amazing English woman who lived with us for a time when I was a child. Her name was Carolyn and she was strong…strong in her beliefs, strong in her faith, strong in her will. She was the daughter of a Methodist vicar who came from England and settled in Navasota, Texas. Carrie, as she was called, married a Baptist minister, who was a widower, twenty years her senior. She had one child, my father.

Carrie was precise in all she did. And not having a daughter, which she so wanted, she instructed me in things she thought important.

"Always stand straight and tall", she would say as she put a book on my head and have me walk with it that way. I remember years later when I was reminded that she was 5'4" tall, I could hardly believe it. I could have sworn she was at least 5'10".

She taught me how to set a "proper" table. It was her belief that meal time was to be a very important time of the day. It was a time for family to sit together and discuss the day. Therefore, it must be treated as such. And for that reason, every meal required a full setting of the table, including cloth napkins. The idea of a tv tray was simply not to be considered. You ate at the table. Period.

Carrie believed that every morning you didn't leave your room until ready for the day. She would get up, get completely dressed (makeup, hair, jewelry, clothes) and then prepare breakfast and begin her day. One morning when she was visiting my husband and me, I had just fed everyone breakfast and gotten my husband off to work and the kids to school. I sat down with a cup of coffee and she said to me, *"You know, Netta, men leave their wives for a reason."* I looked at her, completely confused. *"Why is that, Granny?"* Her answer was priceless. *"The girl they marry is the one they want to see when they leave for work. I've never let my husband see me without my makeup, clothes and jewelry."* Seriously? I didn't laugh because she WAS serious. Now, with all the things I do as a direct influence of Carrie in my life, I'm afraid that is one that never stuck.

Carrie never understood a joke. She did not have a very good sense of humor. And yet she was at times funny. I remember once when she was visiting that she declined to go to church one Sunday. She always went to church. But it was Mother's Day and she had heard they were going to give roses to different mothers that day... the youngest, the oldest, the one with the most children, etc. When my dad asked her why she wasn't going she replied, *"I will not go and be given a flower for being the oldest thing in the building."* The end.

After she was widowed the second time and was living alone, I would sometimes pick her up to run errands (grocery shopping) and have a bite of lunch. One day we were in the grocery store and she was looking at the produce. She asked to speak to the manager of the department. A young man (young to her, by now she was in her 90s) came and introduced himself asking how he could help. She told him the heads of lettuce were too large for just one person and she was wondering if he had some smaller ones or could he just sell her a half a head of lettuce. And by the way, she needed four carrots and two radishes. Could he help her with that? The man looked at me with a "help me out here?" look and I just stared back. He very sweetly explained there were no smaller heads of lettuce and he couldn't break up the produce the way she wanted. She did not understand the problem. We finally solved it by buying everything she wanted and then she and I went home, and I purchased what she did not need. She did NOT believe in waste.

Carrie was a strong Christian. She not only read her Bible every day, she studied it. Having been married to a pastor for many years, she sympathized with what a pastor and his family went through. I never heard her be critical of a pastor...not one time. In her last years she was back in Houston and attended First Baptist. Her pastor was John Bisagno and oh, how she loved her pastor.

She set for me, a wonderful example of the importance of faith in my life. She gave me a Bible very dear to her with instructions it is to be passed down to my daughter, and then to hers, and so on. It was her mother's Bible, printed in 1828. The box it is kept in is probably as old as the Bible. Her instructions, in her hand writing, are in the front of the Bible.

Carrie would sit for an hour during the day and "ponder" the things in her life. She did not stress about things. She believed worry was a waste of time. She believed that each day was a gift from God, and we should spend the day "unwrapping" the gift.

I love that this woman was in my life. Her influence is still strong. As I think of her and the impact she has had on me, I hope my life will impact others, remembering that today I shall continue unwrapping the gift.

This piece is dedicated to the memory of Carolyn Burrows McGinty, a lovely English woman of great faith, strong beliefs, and a joy for living each day as a gift from heaven.

The only photo of Carrie that survived the Hurricane Harvey flood waters in my home.

Unanswered Prayer

by Kristi Endres

Have you ever begged and prayed to God for something that just didn't pan out the way you prayed for in the end? Yeah, me too.

From the outside looking in, you can clearly see that I have the best fortune to have two incredible little boys that call me Mommy. But what you don't see is that I miscarried my first pregnancy. I didn't understand it then when utter devastation was pouring out of my eyes in deep sobs, but that was an unanswered prayer. If I hadn't had that miscarriage, I wouldn't have my second son sleeping soundly in his bed right now. And if I didn't have him, well, let's just say this world would be a lot less bright.

My sweet P was 2 years old when we knew something was different about him. Even after getting a diagnosis of a language delay that year, we had a feeling that there was more to his story. When he was 5, we finally got a diagnosis that made all the puzzle pieces fit together and make sense. Parker was diagnosed with Autism Spectrum Disorder.

Talk about a bittersweet moment. My husband and I were both relieved to finally have a reason for all the "why's" but at the same time were mourning for the life we mistakenly thought was his future. I can't imagine Parker not being who he is, because who he is has taught our family so much of what we never knew we needed until he entered our lives. Parker: train know-it-all, little brother, chocolate ice cream connoisseur, and, last but not least, teacher of many lessons that have changed our lives for the better. Here are only a few of those lessons:

- **BE HONEST.**
  Y'all. This boy is honest to a fault. Sure it makes for some good, deep belly laugh material after the fact when he says something highly inappropriate or embarrassing *(exhibit A: One time, as he handed his candy to the cashier at the gas station, he turned to me and said, "Eee...she's cweepy.")*, but it's times like when I told him, *"I'm so glad that you're my son,"* and he quickly replied, *"I'm so glad you're my mom,"* that I appreciate his honesty so much. When you have a kid with a language delay, there were times we thought he wouldn't be able to express himself, so to have him be able to do so now gives us such an appreciation for his honesty and inability to hide exactly what he's feeling. I always know where he stands, because he always tells the truth, even if it's not pretty and aimed at me. And that's a pretty great character trait if you ask me.

- **APPRECIATE THE SMALL THINGS.**
  Here's the funny thing about small things. They're not really small things at all. They're the big things in life. When you're fighting to

teach your child to say, *"I want milk please"* and count the words on your fingers as you say them to encourage your child to use language when all they're saying at the time is "mok" for "milk", it's easy to get discouraged. But then little things happen that let you know that you're making progress. He's getting it. Bit by bit and experience by experience, he's soaking it all in. Something as simple as teaching him how to play a joke on someone was a lesson learned over time by modeling from his daddy, his brother, and me. For the longest time, he would take jokes personally or just not get why it was funny, but we didn't give up trying. Then, it finally happened. When it was time to brush their teeth before bed one night, Parker took the initiative to put the toothpaste on both his and his brother's toothbrushes. It wasn't long before we heard, *"Gross! What's wrong with this toothpaste?!"* and heard Parker laughing hysterically next to his disgusted brother. When we walked in the bathroom, we quickly realized that Parker had played a prank on his brother. He used hydrocortisone cream on his toothbrush instead of toothpaste! After they went to bed, my husband and I grinned from ear to ear over this small, yet monstrous, victory. You take 'em where you can get 'em and celebrate every step you thought might not be possible for one reason or another, and if you live like that, you're sure to be happy a lot more than not.

- **BE EASY TO FORGIVE.**

So there's this thing with autism where social situations can be a bit tricky sometimes. On more than one occasion, Parker has been knee-deep in a situation where tensions were running high. Those can be rough times to navigate in the moment, but what I love about those moments is what comes at the end—the *"sorry"*. Once he accepts someone's apology, he truly moves on. He doesn't hold grudges and try to get back at them at a later time or throw it in their face when they do something to him again down the road. How amazing is that to not hold on to the negative energy and just choose to truly forgive someone and move on?!

- **HAVE PATIENCE.**

Listen, I thought I was a pretty patient person before I had kids, but I really had no idea what "patient" meant. I thought of it as the typical short time frame patience, but Parker taught me that patience means much more than that. Patience means continuing to believe in something even when it seems impossible. When Parker was 3 and started a preschool program for half days, I'd pick him up and ask him the same question every day: *"What did you do today?"* For a long time, I didn't get any response. I would just talk to him as if we were having a conversation, hoping that one day he'd join me by talking back. The next year, I started getting a response from him where he would parrot what I said. *"Parker, what did you do today?"* and he'd reply with the same intonation I had used with, *"What did you do today?"* More time passed and I would talk as if I was him answering, so he'd get an idea of things he could reply with: *"...Did you play with friends? Did you eat snack? Did you read?"* That's when he started replying by saying those things back to me: *"Play with friends. Eat snack. Read,"* and it was the same response every day. But one day, he changed it up on me. I remember looking at him in my rearview mirror, preparing myself for the memorized version he had on repeat when he said, *"Play with friends outside. I paint."* Holy. Cow. He actually told me what he did that didn't come from memory. Cue the ugly crying. From there, his responses continued to get more real and we finally started having a real conversation about his day, little by little, every day. That's patience. He taught me that.

So, the next time you feel like your prayers are going unanswered, remember that there is something else already lined up for you. Something bigger and better. And if you're as lucky as me, it might come in a little boy package wearing light blue glasses. I'm so grateful for the opportunity to be Parker's mom. Being wrong by wanting something that was never meant to be for me has never been so right. Because of that moment, I have him. He was always meant to be mine, and I love him to infinity and beyond.

Thank you, P, for all of the lessons you've taught me and all of the lessons to come for anyone who is lucky enough to meet you. You are a dream come true for your daddy and me and the perfect built-in best friend for Connar. I love you.

To the Legendary Joe Tremaine

by Tami Richardson

During my senior year of high school, I had the good fortune of attending a Tremaine Dance convention. That convention was absolutely life-changing, thanks to Mr. Joe Tremaine.

Here is a little history of what led up to the convention…

My mother was a former dancer, who had trained at various places during her young life. At 18 years of age, she auditioned to be a showgirl at the world renowned club Blinstrub's in Boston, Massachusetts. She made the audition, as well as the move from her hometown of Texas. It just so happened that my dad was a world-famous trumpet player in the band at Blinstrub's. That is how they met and married. Many of the great entertainers of the time performed in the shows, such as Frank Sinatra, Sammy Davis Junior, Bobby Vinton, Wayne Newton, and numerous others.

Shortly after my parents were married, my mom stopped dancing to raise me and my 2 brothers. Our family moved back to Texas, and my dad continued to play in various bands, and with the Houston Symphony, etc.

My mom put me in ballet classes when I was 5. I wasn't really a natural at ballet, it was challenging, and to be quite honest, boring. I kept taking ballet until I was 10 years old. I got my first set of pointe' shoes, and it was downhill from there! I never could get over the box of those shoes! My mom had just started to sub for my teacher shortly before I quit. She WAS a natural! My mom is very beautiful, elegant, and has a figure to this day that is just incredible! She obviously missed her years of dancing and started to teach dance at our local recreation center. The following year, when I was a freshman in High School, my grandparents opened a dance studio for her.

I began taking various classes in ballet, tap, and jazz. My best friend Suzy and I would help in the young classes for $2.00 an hour. I was in ninth grade at the time and really loved helping with classes. My interest was growing in dance as well as earning money. By age 16, I was teaching my own classes and got in my High School work program. I had been on our high school drill team for a year but decided to quit and pursue dance. I liked all of my dance classes, but there was not really a passion. Dance just seemed a bit boring. But my interest grew when my mom hired a gorgeous firecracker jazz teacher named Delee Lively, she was mesmerizing! I wanted to dance just like her. But shortly after she was hired, she auditioned for "A Chorus Line" on Broadway and got a lead role! She went on to do amazing things but, she sure was missed. After she left, I became the jazz teacher. I had very little experience, but I actually was a natural when it came to jazz dance. I would teach my students the latest "craze" dances like the running man, roger rabbit, cabbage patch LOL (really dating myself). I thought it was important for dancers to learn all styles of jazz. We would even do the Charleston, the twist, the jerk, etc. in combos. I had a great love for all styles of jazz and music. We would do routines to anything from Big band music to classic rock. As much as I loved teaching, there was something missing.

The summer of my senior year, my mom asked me if I wanted to go to a new dance convention that was coming to Dallas. I thought it would be fun, and boy was it!

We got to the lobby of the hotel, and it was like nothing I had ever seen before! When it was time for the first class, we were all ushered into a grand ballroom. There must have been 500 gorgeous dancers. I was VERY intimidated but excited. We were ready for the first class when in walked a slender charismatic man, with reddish brown hair, jazz pants, a bandana, and a flannel shirt wrapped around his waist! It was Joe Tremaine! He introduced himself and explained he was going to teach a routine to "Sing Sing Sing". Big Band Music, yay!

He had a gorgeous assistant on stage with him. As he started, he said, *"Are ya ready? And we have a step kick, step step, step kick step step, head circle 2 3 4…. repeat the step kick and knock your knees together"* His teaching was a lot of fun. He was witty and had a funny sense of humor.

He taught about 6 eight counts and said, *"Watch us do it with the music one time"* … my jaw dropped, the way they moved was unreal. It was hip and fun, but they lit the stage on fire! I had a blast in the class, and actually picked up the choreography. It was fast-paced with quick feet and arm movements. A style I had never had but LOVED! After that class, I went to the lyrical class with a breathtaking young teacher, Mr. Doug Caldwell. He told stories that brought tears to my eyes and danced from his gut and soul. On to the next class with the assistant from Joe's first class. A sultry, drop-dead gorgeous, sassy dancer, Marcia Lane. She also had a style of her own I had never seen. Then on to Jackie Sleight's class. A technical, fun energetic, classic jazz, then tap with Tony who used drums and did handstands and gymnastic moves during his class. SO much fun! And last, but certainly not least, a break-dancing class with Barry Lather. He was probably 16 at the time. That was the easiest class for me because my little brother and his friends were break dancers. I had learned a lot of it. Barry went on to be the hip hop teacher with Tremaine, as well as a choreographer for Janet Jackson and so many more. All of the staff had done incredible things and worked with numerous stars.

At the end of the convention, the staff came out and performed. I had just never seen dancing, energy, fun and talent like that in my life! That convention sparked a fire in me. We started going to Tremaine twice a year and would bring our competitive students. I bought the teaching VHS tapes and studied all the teachers and routines. I was consumed with dance. I began teaching competitive routines for my mom's studio. Choreography was very natural to me. I won numerous choreography awards at competitions. I felt like I was doing what God made me to do! The influence of Tremaine has been with me for the past 40 years of teaching/choreographing, as well as the last 15 as a studio owner. My daughter and

I now work together at the studio I own in Pearland, Texas. My daughter Kassi was just given the title of director. She is carrying on the dance legacy. Turns out she is a little firecracker teacher, and choreographer winning awards everywhere. I am so grateful for the dance, music, and business genetics in my family. Thankful that God has allowed me to dance and do what I love for so many years!

And I am beyond GRATEFUL for the
life-changing gift of dance, energy, and enthusiasm
Mr. Joe Tremaine brought to my life, along with
the entire dance world. He is truly a legend and
his mark will never leave the dance world.

A Story of Two Bean Counters and a Fruit Bearing Tree

by Bryce Tawney

It was a hot drive in mid-June 1980, from Denton to Carrollton in my 1965 Volkswagen Beetle with no air conditioning. I was wearing the only sports jacket I owned. I was a bit nervous about the interview at Otis Engineering, a division of Halliburton. Although my grades were good, I was introverted and lacked self-confidence. I learned about Otis from catalogs in the North Texas State University Career Center. The oil and gas industry was despised during that time, due to the gas embargos, rationing and waiting lines back in the mid-1970s, and reality was that I could not be picky about the industry.

When I arrived, I met with Kay McKinnish from Human Resources. Ms. McKinnish was very welcoming and provided a great introduction to the company. She took me to the Finance building to meet the hiring manager, Charles Muchmore, from Financial Reporting.

Charles made me feel comfortable early on, breaking the ice with banter about growing up in Dallas and working while pursuing a degree. The interview was like a conversation rather than the intimidating interviews I experienced at other companies. Driving back to Denton, I had zero expectations what would happen next. Shortly after arriving home, the phone rang and surprisingly it was Ms. McKinnish. She stated the interview went well and they wanted to extend a job offer. I started on June 26 as an Associate Accountant.

Robert Charles Muchmore, Jr. was my first boss. Charles was a graduate of the School of Business Administration at Southern Methodist University and a Certified Public Accountant who had started his career at Arthur Andersen. In 1978 Charles left public accounting and joined Otis Engineering's Internal Audit Department, and boy was I grateful he did, as it was he who planted the seed of my career.

There were four of us in Charles' group. My tiny desk was behind a six-foot partition in a small space used for storage. I felt comfortable with Charles and folks in the various accounting departments. Charles was a workaholic, I never saw him take breaks, and he rarely joined us for lunch. He was in early and out late. Charles was a patient teacher, with keen technical accounting skills, and was always taking time to help others. Charles was well respected by his peers and executive management. His business manner was frank and to the point. One day while working in my storage closet, I heard Charles from his office across the partition *"Damn it, Bryce!! Get in here!!"* I rushed to his office to find him reviewing my work. By the time I left his office, I knew I had to work harder to meet his high expectations. The sapling tree was growing.

I received a promotion to the Internal Audit Department in February 1981. While disappointed to leave Charles' team, I was excited about learning new skills and traveling to Otis' worldwide locations! In Internal Audit I became less shy and more extroverted. Charles' career also grew as he took roles of increasing responsibility. I left Internal Audit in early 1983 to take a position as Rotational Accountant between Dallas and Paris, France. This opportunity could have easily bypassed me. A couple of months earlier, I was offered and turned down an assignment in Nigeria. Turning down an offer was often a career killer in the 1980s. I was prepared to wait a long time for another international assignment to be offered. It was likely that Charles had to overcome some high political hurdles to make the rotational assignment available to me. For Charles' efforts, I obtained fantastic business and operations experience in that role. One of the most valuable lessons I learned from Charles' leadership was to not bring problems to your manager, but bring them solutions. My career tree flourished with the growth of strong branches.

My rotational assignment became a permanent expatriate assignment in Paris in April 1984. I recall Charles making a business trip to Paris. He wanted to visit several sites over the weekend. Charles had always been adventurous and passionate about hiking and exploring. We visited many sites including what felt like a hundred famous churches including Notre Dame, Sainte Chapelle, Sacre Coeur and La Madeleine. I was physically dragging from exploring so many historical buildings and religious sites! Charles just laughed when I accused him of trying to convert me to a religious zealot!!

Just a few years later in 1989, Halliburton restructured and consolidated the various accounting teams from Otis and other divisions. I had relocated in 1987 to London for Otis and now was headed back to Paris as part of the restructure. Charles earned a regional assignment in London, thereby becoming my boss again. His first year abroad, Charles traveled to Paris to spend Christmas with my family and me. It was very nice and enjoyable to be together as friends while away from our families in Texas.

I was reassigned to Duncan, Oklahoma as a department supervisor in August 1990. I was devastated! I didn't know whether to laugh or cry, so I drank tequila instead!! While I knew one day my career would likely go through Duncan, I was hoping it wouldn't be for a few more years. Charles knew just what to say. He said it would be great career development and provide visibility to Duncan senior management. Charles was right, so I set my mind to make an impression. I held several key positions and worked on several successful strategic projects over nine years in Duncan. I was also deeply involved in university recruiting and creating development programs. As my own career tree matured, I was now planting the seeds for many young accountants joining the company.

I transferred to Houston in early 1999. Charles was already at another office site in a Halliburton Corporate role. My role was in the Energy Services Group. Charles came to Energy Services Corporate with the split off of KBR in 2007. It was a time of significant change within

Halliburton. During these chaotic times, Charles provided exceptional collaborative leadership. He had the respect of the accounting directors, vice presidents, and their teams. He was instrumental in transforming the company in response to new accounting regulations. He was relied upon heavily by each new CFO, but in time, change begot change. Charles left Halliburton in 2007, and my 36-year career at Halliburton ended in 2016 when I retired.

While infrequent, our paths still crossed. In 2018 after Charles joined his current company, he called to inquire about a job opportunity on his accounting team. Regrettably, the timing was not right although I was very tempted. I could only imagine being back in the office with Charles, with him calling out to me.... *"Damn it, Bryce, get in here!!"*

It's 2019 and I am retired, enjoying lake life and fishing at our beautiful lake home. I am thankful to be enjoying the rich fruit from the tree Charles planted over 38 years ago.

Dedicated to Charles Muchmore, Jr., my friend, mentor and professional role model. Thank you for planting the seed for my career.

Finding Gratitude by Looking Back

by Corinne O'Flynn

When I was five years old, my mom took me to our local branch of the New York Public Library in the Bronx. I remember two things about that day with perfect clarity. First, was sitting at a long wooden table next to a teenage girl with a big plastic comb in her hair. She had sky blue ribbons woven around the comb; the shiny ends hung down and mingled with her glamorous feathered hair.

The other memory was pulling The Snowy Day by Ezra Jack Keats off the shelf. I loved the bright illustrations and Peter who donned his red snowsuit with the pointed hood and set off alone to explore his blizzard-blanketed city. I especially loved the part where he packed a snowball into his pocket for tomorrow only to find it had melted overnight.

Pocket snowballs and blue ribbons in feathered hair mark the beginning of my journey into a love of reading. I credit my mom for all the things that led me to books. She always had a book in one hand and a Parliament 100 cigarette in the other. Like pocket snowballs, memories of my mom are forever entwined with memories of books.

When I was nine years old, I stayed home sick. My parents worked and my three sisters went to school, so I was home alone in our apartment. If my mom had been a reader of romance or women's fiction, my journey as a writer might have gone in a completely different direction. I might be sharing with you how I pulled one of her books from the bookcase, and through pages I was too young to read, discovered the magical wonder of steamy sex scenes and the thrilling pangs of first love.

But that isn't what happened.

Instead, there I was, all alone in our apartment, curled up under the covers, devouring Salem's Lot by Stephen King with a white-knuckle grip—transfixed, and paralyzed with delicious fear. I fell into fantasy and paranormal suspense and never looked back.

When she wasn't reading, my mom loved to play word games, Scrabble especially. In my early twenties, we started a tradition of Scrabble marathons. We'd sit at her kitchen table for hours and play game after game. By the end of the night, the ashtray would be full and there wouldn't be enough room on the table for another snack.

The Official Scrabble Player's Dictionary was stored inside her deluxe game box, and we'd talk about our letters and help each other maximize each move as we swiveled the board back and forth.

It's how I discovered my love of obscure words. It's also where I played the most valuable word I have ever played: Caziques. It's got the Z and the Q, and I got it with double letter points on the Z and then triple word, on top of the fifty bonus points for a bingo. It was a religious experience—one my mom totally understood.

One night, during a seriously long scrabble marathon that lasted well into the wee hours, I studied my rack and looked up at my mom. Sensing my question, she looked up at me.

"*Rhon,*" I said.

She tapped the ash off her cigarette. "*Rhon?*"

"*Rhon,*" I repeated.

"*Spell it,*" she said.

So I did, "*R. A. N.*"

"*Hmm. Rhon,*" she said, nodding. "*I don't know. Look it up.*"

I reached for the dictionary on the table and she stopped me, shooing me with her cigarette hand, the smoke zig-zagging between us. "*It won't be in there. Check the Unabridged.*"

She called it the Unabridged with a capital U.

The Unabridged lay open on the counter by the fireplace like a bible. The spotlight in the ceiling shone down, giving the pages an ethereal glow. I fingered the tab cutout to get to the section. I ran my finger over tissue-thin pages and stopped when I found it.

I read it aloud. "*Rhon (Ran). Verb. Simple past tense of run.*"

We gaped at each other while our brains reconciled the dissonance of what I had just said. Then, while the three A.M. house was dark and asleep, my mother howled with laughter. Soon, the two of us were wiping tears from our eyes, doubled over cross-legged to keep from wetting our pants.

My mom was the one who wanted to be a writer. She had a notebook where she stored all the ideas and some snippets of a story she dreamed of developing into a novel one day. She died two months after her fifty-first birthday, only five short years after that night with the Unabridged. She never wrote her novel.

The following year, just after the anniversary of my mom's death, my daughter died. The year after that, while I was pregnant with my son, I had a dream.

In the dream, a little boy stood in the tall grass of the mountain foothills. The sun was almost touching the top of the mountains and the sky was sunset orange. Beside him in the grass stood a tiger, and in the air next to them, hovering on the wind, was a falcon. In my dream, the boy was communicating with both animals using his mind.

This visual vignette stayed with me—haunting me on a regular basis. I saw it while I did the laundry, while in the shower, it appeared while I was stopped at red lights, and I saw it all the time after my son was born when the days became a blur of breastfeeding and diapers and sleepless haze. This scene with the boy thrummed in my subconscious and did not stop until I wrote it down. It was like my mom smiled, and the Universe whisper-screamed "FINALLY."

The vignette stopped chasing me and my story bloomed inside my head. At a time when everything creative in me had shut down, it was transformative to have tapped into this wild stream of free-flowing story.

Fourteen years later, my first book was published in October, shortly after my mother's birthday. It features a boy, his tiger, and a falcon. Holding that book in my hand was bittersweet. Of course, the feeling of personal achievement was intense, but the person who made it possible in every way, the person who would have understood best what it meant to me wasn't there.

If my mom were alive today, she'd probably be that mom who carried a box of my books in the trunk of her car and sold them to strangers like cartons of illegal cigarettes.

In October 2017, just in time for what would have been my mom's 70th birthday, the US Postal Service issued a set of stamps honoring Ezra Jack Keats. They feature images of Peter from The Snowy Day. I learned about it at the counter mailing a signed copy of my book to a friend.

The two most important days in your life are the day you are born and the day you find out why. – Mark Twain

For me, "why" is laden with meaning and wrapped in deep gratitude.

For my mother, whose lifelong love of words
and story was baked into me from the start.

My True Dad

by Joyce Barbazette

Typically, one thinks of their dad as being the person who is their biological father and has been with them since birth. Well, that's not the case with me. My true dad came into my life when I was eleven years old, just about to turn 12. His name was Albert Edward Mead, and we called him Eddie.

I am from Columbus, Ohio and my parents divorced when I was 10. My mom knew Eddie from 20 years before and even though he lived in Texas, he found out about the divorce and contacted her. I was young, so I am not sure of all the details, but I believe they long-distance dated for a couple of months when my mom announced, *"We're moving to Houston, Texas."* It was a lot to take in all at once because we met Eddie about the same time that we were moving to Texas to live with him as our stepfather. Eddie had already been divorced and had been living in Houston for seven years. I guess to him and my mom it made sense for my mom, me, my little brother, and my little sister to join him in Houston (my older siblings stayed in Ohio). I had only met Eddie a time or two before we moved. Amazingly though, our relationship was good from the start. While it took some getting to know his ways and strictness, it was all right.

It didn't take long for Eddie to become the one that was always there for me. Even though I would still see my biological father for a couple of weeks each summer until I graduated from high school, Eddie was the one my friends knew, and the one who was in my day-to-day life. I always maintained a relationship with my "real" dad, but Eddie was my true Dad. Although he had his own children, actually five of them, I never felt like the "step child". His kids often visited us in Texas and a couple of them even lived with us for a time. Even when his kids were around, we were always treated the same; you would never know we weren't his biological children.

The memories I have of my school days are filled with Eddie and his involvement as a parent. He even dressed up like a girl and performed a dance at my high school drill team banquet. That memory still makes me cry every time I think about it. It was so special. Eddie was <u>always</u> in the audience to watch me dance! He is the dad who was there to give me away at my weddings (yes, plural), and he was there when they fell apart. And when I needed a person to lean on that loved me and understood me, it was Eddie that I called, and who was always there. He is the one that helped me through my illnesses, and I truly missed him when he died during my breast cancer treatments. However, I know he was my angel and never left my side during that time.

When my girls, Jamie and Jodie, think of their grandfather, they think of Eddie. Their other grandfather is referred to as "Grandpa in Ohio". Not to say my biological dad loved my girls any less than Eddie, because he did love them, it's just that their relationship with him was different than it was with Eddie. Eddie was there at their births and throughout their lives, and he was <u>always</u> in the audience to watch them dance too! Unfortunately, he was only able to meet one of my grandchildren – my first, Hunter. Eddie passed away in 1999 while both of my daughters were pregnant for the next set of grandkids. However, Papaw Eddie is part of the vocabulary for the other grandchildren. He is still often talked about, as he was an integral part of our lives.

It was Eddie who got my daughter, Jodie out of the hospital in time for Christmas when she was just two years old. Jodie was hospitalized because of severe dehydration from a stomach virus and had been there for three days. The doctors would not release her until she was able to eat on her own. Her dad and I tried to get her to eat, but we weren't successful. However, Eddie tried, and she ate. He sat with her on the bed and spoon-fed her. It took him to make her eat and to get her up and going. Thanks to Eddie, she was able to be released the next day, in time for Christmas.

I am so grateful for this man, Eddie. The man who I let everyone know was my dad so very easily. My siblings (another five of them) and their children have similar stories and feel the same way I do. We all thought of Eddie as our dad. I am also grateful for that. It is not often the entire family thinks of a stepdad so highly. He made it wonderful for all us. Even though he was not there at my birth, Eddie was what a dad should be – MY TRUE DAD!

To Eddie, the man who raised me
and loved me like his own.

Inquiring Minds Want to Know...

AKA FAQs

What does Gratitude 540 mean?

Author David Hawkins, MD., Ph.D. shared some incredible work with us over his lifetime. In his level of consciousness teachings, he shared that love vibrates at a consciousness level of 500 on a scale from 1-1,000. He tells us that most of humanity is calibrating around 200, which is where courage starts emerging. Gratitude vibrates at 540 and is a golden key to raising your own vibration and living into your authentic purpose. Hawkins shares that when each of us works to raise our own consciousness level, we assist others in rising with us.

Why a butterfly on the cover?

Around the world, people identify the butterfly as representing endurance, change, hope, and life. When you engage in a regular gratitude practice, hope and wonder are reignited. This new flame is often a catalyst for some level of change or realignment regarding what you do and who you are.

What is the symbol in the 0 spot of 540?

This is a symbol that I channeled and drew myself. I created it for my gratitude journals and it can now be seen throughout all of my gratitude work. You will see it in many places soon: jewelry, dinnerware, giftables, etc.

Why practice gratitude?

Science has caught up and now can demonstrate in measurable ways that gratitude increases happiness, reduces depression, and builds resilience. I have also seen the direct impact on my own self- awareness journey and hundreds of others I have supported in their own inner journey. As patterns emerge in your practice, new awarenesses will also arrive. Your new consciousness will spark your sense of curiosity and inevitably shift the way you look at the world. Curiosity is a way of bringing more awe and wonder into our world. You feel the wonder, then you feel grateful for the wonder. As gratitude is experienced and expressed, choices expand.

How do I start a gratitude practice?

One of the most common entry points is through journaling. One form, is called free form journaling, which means blank pages in a book that you write as little or as much and as often as you like. Another style is guided journaling, which means that the creator/author takes you through prompts for your own practice. For an example of that, you can check out the journals I created here: https://alexsysthompson.com/gratitude-series.

If writing isn't your thing, there are also meditative forms of gratitude, as well as some great gratitude aps. And there is always the old-fashioned verbal expression of gratitude.

Thank you for being here on the journey with me. I hope these stories light a spark in your heart and soul.

Gratefully yours,
Alexsys

Made in the USA
Middletown, DE
29 August 2020

17477534R00092